book a *V*ision book a *V*ision book a *V*ision book a *V*ision book

book a *V*ision book a *V*ision book

book a *V*ision book a *V*ision book a *V*ision book a *V*ision book

book a *V*ision book a *V*ision book a *V*ision book a *V*ision book

book a *V*ision book a *V*ision book a *V*ision book a *V*ision book

book a *V*ision book a *V*ision book a *V*ision book a *V*ision book

ook a *V*ision book a *V*ision book a *V*ision book a *V*ision book

ook a *V*ision book a *V*ision book a *V*ision book a *V*ision book

ook a *V*ision book a *V*ision book a *V*ision book a *V*ision book

ook a *V*ision book a *V*ision book a *V*ision book a *V*ision book

ook a *V*ision book a *V*ision book a *V*ision book a *V*ision book

ook a *V*ision book a *V*ision book a *V*ision book a *V*ision book

ok a *V*ision book a *V*ision book a *V*ision book a *V*ision book

ok a *V*ision book a *V*ision book a *V*ision book a *V*ision book

ok a *V*ision book a *V*ision book a *V*ision book a *V*ision book

ok a *V*ision book a *V*ision book a *V*ision book a *V*ision book

k a *V*ision book a *V*ision book a *V*ision book a *V*ision book

k a *V*ision book a *V*ision book a *V*ision book a *V*ision book

k a *V*ision book a *V*ision book a *V*ision book a *V*ision book

k a *V*ision book a *V*ision book a *V*ision book a *V*ision book

St. Augustine
and His Search for Faith

MILTON LOMASK has written:

St. Isaac and the Indians
John Carroll: Bishop and Patriot

St. Augustine

and His Search for Faith

by *Milton Lomask*

illustrated by *Johannes Troyer*

VISION BOOKS

Farrar, Straus & Cudahy · *New York*

Burns & Oates · *London*

*For the children of Joe and Lee Neville,
namely, Francis, Susan, Gail and Bruce*

Contents

Author's Note

Most of the facts of St. Augustine's life in this book were taken from the Doctor of Grace's own writings, notably, *The Confessions of St. Augustine* (the 1909 Harvard Classics edition published by Collier), *The City of God* (the Modern Library edition edited by Thomas Merton), those letters of St. Augustine which are reprinted in Anne Fremantle's *A Treasury of Early Christianity* (Viking, 1953), and from the sermons quoted by Sister Marie Madeleine Getty in her "The Life of the North Africans as Revealed in the Sermons of St. Augustine" (Catholic University of America *Patristic Studies*, v. 28, 1931).

For further facts about St. Augustine, the author turned to a number of books and articles. Chief among these were *Augustine's Quest for Wisdom*, a remarkably informative study by Dr. Vernon Joseph Burke (Bruce, 1945), *Young Augustine* by John J. O'Meara (Longmans, Green,

1954), and *Saint Augustine* by Giovanni Papini (Harcourt, Brace, 1930). Those sections of the story in which St. Ambrose figures were based partly on St. Augustine's own accounts and partly on volumes 1 and 2 of John Henry Cardinal Newman's *Historical Sketches* (Longmans, Green, 1897-8).

The description of the Carthage of Augustine's day was taken from Gaston Boissier's *Roman Africa* (Putnam, 1899). Boissier's vivid book is based on the findings of nineteenth-century archeologists. As for the descriptions of Tagaste—Augustine's home town—those, too, were borrowed from Boissier, although in an indirect way. Today the Algerian trading village of Souk-Ahras stands on the site of Tagaste, but of Tagaste itself we know nothing. Archeologists, however, have dug up the ruins of a similar city called Timgad, and what we know about Timgad has been used in this book to give the reader some idea of the town where Augustine grew up and where he founded his first monastery.

Other books used by the author because of their helpfulness in reconstructing Augustine's era were Henryk Sienkiewicz's novel *Quo Vadis* (Little, Brown, 1949) and J. Carcopino's *Daily Life in Ancient Rome* (Yale University Press, 1940).

The stanza of the *Te Deum* quoted on page 177 is from *The Hymns of the Breviary and Missal* (Benziger, 1949), edited by Dom Matthew Britt, O.S.B. (translation by Clarence Alphonsus Walforth, C.S.P.).

St. Augustine
and His Search for Faith

1. The Bishop of Hippo

Augustine, the bishop of Hippo in North Africa, wrote the words "The End" at the bottom of a long parchment. In his vigorous scrawl he wrote the name of the month, which was August, and the number of the year, which, as *anno Domini* 400, meant 400 years after the birth of our Lord.

Dropping his reed pen, he opened and closed the fingers of his hand, tired with long hours of writing. He had sat down at his stone desk after supper the night before. It was dawn now. A pale, gray light drifted through the window of his bedroom-study.

He turned in his chair as he heard a shuffling sound in the hall behind him. "Brother Porter," he called, "is that you?"

Brother Porter came in, carrying a broom made of twigs and shrubbery. He was a doll-like old man, and one of his legs was shorter than the other.

"You are up early," the bishop said.

Brother Porter made a clucking sound, shaking his head. "No, your lordship," he said, "I am not up early. You are up late." He clucked again. "Last night," he went on, "you spent half the night writing. You did the same the night before and the night before that. When are you going to get yourself some sleep?"

The bishop laughed. Although he was forty-six years old, his laugh was as boisterous as a boy's. "I will get plenty of sleep now," he said. "I have finished my book."

"God be thanked." Brother Porter limped to the desk. He ran his eyes over the parchments there. "You write so many books," he said. "What is this one about?"

"Me," the bishop replied. "This book is the story of my life."

"God be praised! What do you call it? Have you a title for the book?"

"Yes, Brother Porter. I call it *My Confessions*."

Brother Porter's eyes flew wide open. He stared in amazement at the bishop. "Have I suddenly gone deaf?" he inquired. "Or did I hear you say that you call your book . . . ?"

"*My Confessions*," the bishop repeated.

"But you are such a good man. What have you to confess?"

The bishop shook his head. "Don't call me a good man. Say rather that I am a man who tries to be good." He picked up one of the parchments. "When you read this," he said with a smile, "you will learn that there was a time when I didn't even try. For the first thirty years of my life I was a conceited and self-willed rascal."

"You, your lordship?"

"I, Brother Porter."

With a quivering forefinger the old man indicated the parchment in the bishop's hand. "And you admit as much in your book? You say there that in your younger days you were a . . ." Brother Porter broke off. He could not bring himself to call the holy bishop of Hippo a wicked man.

The bishop said it for him. "In my youth," he told Brother Porter, "I did many wicked things.

I have tried to describe all of them in my book."

"Your readers will not believe you."

"I hope they do. I hope they are cheered by what I have written." The bishop's lean face became sober. It was the face of a member of the African Berber tribe, with a Berber's bronze skin and faded blue eyes under a tumble of reddish curls.

"You see, Brother Porter," he said, "I wrote this book for a reason. I want to show people that no matter how bad a man is, he can always become better. He has only to turn to God, and God will help him."

The smile returned to the bishop's lips. "Remember, Brother Porter, our Lord's story about the farmer who lost a sheep out of his huge flock? Remember how pleased he was to find that one sheep? So it is with every sinner who turns back to God. As our Lord told His disciples, 'there will be joy in heaven over one sinner who repents.'"

Seeing that the bishop was about to rise, Brother Porter pulled back his chair for him. "And now, your lordship," he said, "it is still an hour till first Mass. You must get some sleep."

"No, thank you." The bishop dropped a friendly hand on the old man's shoulder. He left the room. His firm stride carried him quickly down a hall into a small garden shaded with date palms and ilex trees.

On the steps of his cathedral he stopped a moment. Shielding his eyes with a hand, he looked out over the shining harbor that made the city of Hippo one of the busiest and prettiest ports on the Mediterranean Sea.

Inside the church he knelt before the tabernacle. He thanked God for permitting him to finish his book. He thanked his mother whom he now thought of as his helper in heaven. It was her prayers years before, the bishop knew, that had given him the strength to turn away from the God-less life he had lived so long.

For a long while he remained on his knees. Then, rising, he seated himself on a velvet-padded chair that was really a niche in the sanctuary wall.

He closed his eyes. The events he had described in his book—the events of his own life—marched through his mind in a series of pictures. What a scoundrel he had been as a boy! What heartaches he had caused his mother—yes, and his father and his many friends!

He smiled. His smile was half amused, half sad, for he was thinking about a day when he was only twelve years old—the day he talked back to the teacher. . . .

2. "Two and Two Are Five!"

The day Augustine talked back to the teacher fell in the year 366. As usual he rose early. There was still dew on the wheat fields as he left his parents' farmhouse followed by Scipio, the slave who took him back and forth to school.

Augustine walked fast. Scipio was old and fat. He huffed and puffed trying to keep up.

"Woe is me!" he wailed as they reached the archway under the cement aqueduct which carried water to the nearby city of Tagaste. "Please, little master, do not go so fast. You are only a boy of twelve summers. But look at me. Sixty long winters have passed over my head."

Augustine was already half a hundred feet in advance. Instead of slowing up his pace, he increased it. "Maybe something has passed *over* your head, Scipio," he shouted over his shoulder, "but I'm sure nothing has ever got *into* it. If you had any sense, you wouldn't eat so much. Then you could walk like a human being."

Their route was down a gentle slope, green with the vivid green of North Africa in spring. Clumps of olive trees and towering pines shaded their path.

They entered the city by the south gate. Tagaste was like every North African city ruled by the emperor in far-off Rome. It was a little Rome itself. Its marble buildings rose steep as cliffs along the streets. At this hour it was busier and noisier than it would be all the rest of the day. Ox-drawn carts, heaped with goods for the market place, were pouring through every gate. Riding horses and chariots dashed by, carrying business men to their shops and city magistrates to the forum where the public buildings stood.

Already the temples were busy. For half a century now the people of the Roman world had enjoyed freedom of religion. Christians were no longer persecuted. Even so, many citizens of Tagaste remained pagans. From far and near they came to worship in temples dedicated to many imaginary gods.

Upon reaching the narrow alleys of the market place, Augustine slowed down for the first time. He loved the market. He loved it more than any other part of the city—more than the theater or the music hall, more than the amphitheater (the circus as most people called it) where even now the horse races and the gladiatorial fights were getting under way.

Eyes darting in all directions, he happily drifted past the open stalls, each with its dazzling array of things for sale. He stared wide-eyed at a row of togas, long and heavy robes that only important men wore. He stared at an exhibit of many-colored tunics, those long and belted blouses that every-body wore—men, women and children.

At a food shop he purchased a drink of water sweetened with fig juice. He was still there when a huff and a puff behind him told him that Scipio had at long last caught up.

The old slave approached with his customary song. "Woe is me! Woe is me! Little master, do you never look at a sundial?"

"Why should I, Scipio?"

"Because time passes. Another minute and you'll be late for school."

"And what if I am?"

"The teacher will whip you again. That's what."

Augustine made a face. "True." He sighed in an exaggerated way. "The teacher has no brains, but he has lots of muscle. His whippings are fierce." He gave old Scipio a jolting nudge in his stomach. "I'll meet you in the usual place when school lets out."

He darted into the crowd. Scipio ran after him. "One minute, little master," he cried. "Your mother gave you a coin. She said you were to give it to me so I could buy my breakfast."

"Did she now!" Augustine had halted some distance away. He knew very well that his mother had given him a coin for Scipio. He also knew that he had spent it at the food shop. "Alas, Scipio," he called, "your coin is in my stomach now. Better there than in yours where there is already too much."

He was off again, leaving old Scipio crooning to himself, "Woe is me! Woe is me!"

The schoolhouse stood on one of the narrow market-place streets. It was not a house; in fact, it was not much of a school. Its roof was a wooden awning attached to one of the buildings. Hanging from this, a dirty canvas, striped like a carnival tent, separated the schoolroom from the rest of the street. The students, some twenty in all, sat on benches at long tables. Up front were two armchairs, a desk, and a blackboard.

As he entered the enclosure, the last boy to arrive, Augustine found that things were not as usual this morning. The teacher was sitting in the smaller of the two armchairs. The other, where he ordinarily sat, held a much older man—a heavy, stoop-shouldered man wearing a snow-white toga.

Augustine took his place alongside his friend Alypius in the rear row. On the table before him, as before each of the boys, was a waxed tablet and a pointed reed for writing.

Talking was forbidden, but Augustine and Alypius had become skilled at using their tablets for that purpose. Making sure that the teacher was not looking his way, Augustine scratched hastily on his.

"Who is the stranger?" he wrote.

Alypius did not turn his head. Keeping his fresh and open face straight forward, he moved his eyes to read Augustine's words. He, too, made sure the teacher was not looking before scribbling his reply.

"One of the city magistrates," he wrote.

Augustine was about to write, "Why is he here?" when he saw that the teacher had risen. Standing in front of the desk, the teacher rapped for attention with his long stick—his ferule, as he called it.

He was a young man with a narrow face and narrow eyes. "Greetings in the name of Caesar," were his first words. The present ruler of the vast Roman world was Valentinian the First but, like all Roman emperors, he was usually spoken of as Caesar.

"This morning," the teacher said, "we have a distinguished visitor, a member of the city council." He nodded toward the old man in the larger armchair. "At the request of the other city magistrates, he has come to inspect our little school. He has come to make certain that I, your teacher, am using the newest and best methods of instruction." The teacher's voice was thin and rather high. It grew higher as he went on, emphasizing his remarks with frequent gestures.

"I have told our visitor," he said, "that you are good students. I have told him how, drinking in my instruction, your minds have opened up and expanded. Even as the flowers open up under the falling rain. Even as the earth expands under the shining sun. Even as . . ."

Without taking his eyes from the teacher's face, Augustine reached for his reed. He scribbled a single word on his tablet.

The word was "windbag." When Alypius saw it, he was taken by surprise. He burst into a loud and tinkling giggle.

The teacher halted in the midst of another flight of oratory. His narrow eyes fell hard on Alypius. Every boy in the room held his breath. Augustine was certain that once the teacher got over his shock, he would come to the rear. He would drag Alypius from his seat and beat him unmercifully.

To his surprise the teacher remained where he was. True, he gulped for air a number of times as though he were having trouble finding his voice. At length, however, he went on, filling the canvas-enclosed room with sound and the air with gestures.

He expressed the hope that all the students were well prepared for the day's lessons. He asked them to "shine" before the distinguished visitor—"to shine even as the moon shines when she comes to us at her fullest and in her brightest raiment." He ended his speech with a razzle-dazzle of gestures, asked the visiting city magistrate to say a few words, and sat down.

The magistrate did not leave his chair. "I'm happy, lads," he said in a low and rolling voice, "to hear that you are good students. I am even happier to hear something else about your school."

He edged forward a little. "When I was a schoolboy," he went on, "I received many whippings. Personally I do not believe in them. I think a good teacher can control his class without much physical punishment. Therefore I am delighted to hear from your teacher himself that no whippings are given in this school."

He sat back, indicating that his talk was done. There was a stir among the boys. None spoke, but every lad glanced at his neighbors.

Augustine was furious. "What a liar the teacher is," he thought, "to say that he gives no whippings." In a school term that lasted nearly eleven months of the year, he himself received almost as many whippings as there were days in the term.

The teacher was on his feet again. "All right now, scholars," he said. "We will start with arithmetic. When you hear your name, rise." He aimed his ferule at a small, towheaded boy in the center of the room. "Vinicius," he said.

Vinicius clambered to his feet. He was a good student, which was probably why the teacher had picked on him first.

"All right," the teacher said, "on with your thinking cap, Vinicius. How much are eighteen and a half and twenty and one-fourth? It's a hard question. If you like, I shall write the numbers on the board."

"No need of that, master." Vinicius addressed the teacher by his proper title. He thought a few seconds. "Eighteen and a half and twenty and one-fourth," he said finally, "are thirty-eight and three-fourths."

The teacher permitted himself one of his rare smiles. His eyes roamed the room, coming to rest on the rear row.

"Augustine!"

Augustine rose. He knew that the teacher considered him his brightest pupil. He braced himself for a hard question.

"Augustine," the teacher said, "I am going to give you a vacation today. How much . . . " He paused. He shot a playful glance at the city magistrate as though to warn him that a joke was coming. "How much," he said again, "are two and two?"

In the split second it took him to get over his surprise, a scheme took possession of Augustine's mind. The teacher had told the magistrate that he never gave whippings. Very well! He would give the teacher a silly answer. He would tease him, taunt him. He would do this until the teacher lost his temper and gave him a whipping—thus showing the magistrate what a liar the teacher was.

"Two and two, master," he said with an expression as innocent as an angel's, "are five!"

The instructor blinked. "Augustine," he said in a pained voice, "you really must listen to me. I notice that you have been writing a good deal on your tablet this morning. No doubt you are composing an ode. No doubt you are creating some masterpiece that will make the *Aeneid*, the great poem by our beloved Virgil, seem a mere trifle in comparison. I must ask you to forget your literary labors. Listen now to my simple question: how much are two and two?"

Augustine answered in the same sweet voice and with the same angelic expression as before. "Two and two," he said, "are five."

The teacher sighed. "I will put the question in another way." He held his right hand up, extending two fingers. "Now," he said, "how many fingers of my right hand are lifted in the air?"

"Two," Augustine replied.

The teacher held up his other hand, extending two fingers. "And how many of the left hand?" he asked.

"Two," was the reply.

"And now, Augustine, how many fingers in all do I have lifted in the air?"

"Five!"

There was a dead silence. That is, there was silence within the classroom itself. The canvas which formed its walls was thin. Ceaselessly the din of the market place outside flooded into the school.

The teacher's narrow eyes were glued on Augustine. He bit his lips. He was already perspiring, for the day was hot. Now additional beads of water popped out on his forehead. His whole body quivered.

"Augustine, son of Patricius!" he roared. "Come forward!"

Augustine paced to the front of the room. He stood before the teacher, a half-smile on his full, delicately-curved lips.

"Now!" the teacher shouted. "You are close to me. You cannot pretend to be blind or deaf. Once more and for the last time: two and two are . . . ?"

Augustine did not wait for the teacher to finish. He simply shouted, "Five!"

The teacher's hair-trigger temper did the rest. Forgetting the lie he had told the magistrate—forgetting, indeed, the magistrate's very presence—he lifted his arm. His ferule fell with a stinging slash across Augustine's shoulder.

Even as Augustine felt the bite of it, he heard a movement behind him. The magistrate, he knew, had risen. The teacher, suddenly remembering his guest, did not strike again. He looked around with a dazed expression. "Now what have I done?" Augustine heard him mutter to himself.

"Go on!" he screamed at the teacher. "Beat me! Beat all of us. You do every day anyhow. Why not today? Telling the magistrate you never whip us! It was a lie, and you know it!"

Augustine stopped, feeling strong hands on both of his arms. He was being slowly turned around. He found himself looking into the wrinkled face of the magistrate.

"My boy, my boy!" The old man's voice rolled over him like a soft cloud. "This is a dreadful thing you are doing. Tell me, my boy, are you a Christian?"

"A Christian?" Augustine shrugged. "Yes and no," he said. "When I was born, the sign of the cross was made over me. The salt of the catechumens was placed on my mouth. But I have not been baptized. When I grow up I don't know what I shall be. Perhaps a Christian like my mother. Perhaps a pagan like my father. I'll decide for myself when I get around to it."

"Your mother, you say, is a Christian?"

"Oh, yes. She is forever praying and going to the basilica, as she calls her church."

"Then, no doubt, she has taught you the sayings of our Lord Jesus Christ?"

"She talks of nothing else. But what has that to do with the teacher? He lied, didn't he?"

A sigh fluttered from the magistrate's lips. "What the teacher does," he said quietly, "is between him and his conscience. You have been unkind, and there is never any excuse for that. Moreover, you are a mere boy. You have committed the grave sin of disrespect for your elders and for authority. Last but not least, you have shown that you have not learned to control yourself. Believe me, my boy, until you have learned that, you have learned nothing."

The soft voice rolled away into silence. Augustine felt shame, but the feeling was short-lived. Back in his seat he stared glumly into space. Soon defiance was strong in him once again. "Figs!" he told himself. "I'm not sorry I did it at all. I'm glad! The silly old teacher had it coming to him!"

3. The Hero

Augustine had not heard the last of his outburst at the teacher. He discovered this at noon when school let out. As he stepped into the bright street of the market place, he was surrounded by cheering boys. Student after student wanted to shake his hand. One thumped him so heartily on the back that he all but lost his balance. The magistrate had called his outburst unkind. Most of his classmates thought otherwise. In their eyes Augustine was a hero.

He walked home as usual with Alypius. They went first to the public baths. There Scipio and the slaves belonging to the other members of the class had spent the morning snoozing and gossiping on the marble porch.

The noon sun was broiling hot. The streets, so busy in the early morning, were all but deserted now. The boys, followed by their slaves, idled through the market place and along the main street. They were in no hurry. Lunch would not be served at home until the heat of the day had passed.

A short distance beyond the city gate they found a group of boys playing on a harpastum court. "What do you say we join them?" Augustine cried, taking to his heels. Alypius ran after him. They spent the next hour playing a basketball-like game, using a chunky ball—the harpastum—filled with sand.

Alypius, too, was pleased with his friend's attack on the teacher. For a time after they left the harpastum court, he talked of nothing else.

"To be sure," he said in his chirpy, bubbly voice, "it's high time someone told the teacher off. On the other hand, I can't help but feel a little worried."

Augustine threw him a sharp glance. Almost the same age—Alypius was a year and a half younger—and sons of families living on adjoining farms, the two were always together. "By all the heroes," Augustine snorted, "you are the world's champion gloom-spreader. First you tell me it's a great thing I did. Now you say it worries you. What worries you about it?"

"Your parents."

"My . . . ?"

"They won't like your talking that way to the teacher."

"Who's to tell them?"

"Who, indeed!" Alypius shot a quick glance toward the rear.

Turning in the direction of his friend's glance, Augustine could see their slaves following at a short distance. "Figs!" he exclaimed. "You don't mean . . . ?"

"Who else?"

"But Scipio wasn't there when it happened. He was two blocks away on the porch of the public baths."

"All the boys didn't wait to congratulate you, Augustine. Some went after their slaves the minute school ended. They must have said something. Their slaves must have told the others, so . . ."

Augustine interrupted. "Oh, figs!" he exclaimed

again. His tone, however, was bolder than his thoughts. What Alypius had said was true. News traveled fast among the slaves, and if old Scipio knew . . . !

As was true of most small cities in Roman-ruled North Africa, few citizens of Tagaste lived in the city itself. It was their trading post and meeting place. The old pagan temples were there and the Catholic basilica, recently built on the main street. The people went into the city to buy and sell, to find entertainment, to take part in civic festivities in the forum. But most of them lived in the country—in the farmhouses and villas scattered over the rolling plateau beyond the city walls.

Augustine's home commanded a low hill a mile from the city gate. The main building, the villa in which the family lived, was a rambling structure of uncut stones under a tile roof. Behind it, a smaller building housed the slaves. A pillared portico joined the buildings. There were many windows but no glass. Heavy draperies curtained the openings during the brief winter. Drawn back now to let in the air, the draperies quivered in a gentle breeze.

Surrounding the buildings were the fields from which Augustine's father earned a barely satisfactory living. Sheep grazed in a small pasture. There was an even smaller wheat field and some vine-yards.

Close by the family villa, neatly trimmed fig-tree hedges created a small checkerboard of gardens, each with its fish pool or fountain. A wooden summerhouse stood at the foot of the broad steps leading into the atrium, the main room of the house.

As Augustine arrived home, he entered the main garden in his usual manner. Climbing onto the iron gate, he loosened the latch and let the gate swing him in. He hopped off and walked on. Scipio, he knew, would close the gate behind him.

Crossing the atrium into the center hall, Augustine went at once to his bedroom at the rear of the villa. There he removed his sleeveless tunic and washed himself in a bowl of water on the marble-topped table. He was lying on his sleeping couch, wearing his loin cloth, when Scipio came in.

The old slave carried a bowl of perfumed olive oil. He kneaded the boy's legs and arms and anointed them with the oil.

"There, now, little master," he said in his mournful voice, "you are ready to have lunch with your good mother and father."

"One minute, Scipio!"

Scipio had reached the curtained doorway. He turned back. "Yes, little master?"

"While you were waiting for me this morning, did you hear anything? I mean, did you hear any special news?"

"Special?" Scipio's lips moved in and out as they always did when he was thinking. His old eyes brightened. "Why, yes, little master," he said excitedly, "there was special news this morning. Would you believe it? The emperor has signed a treaty with King Shapur of Persia. There will be no more war between our two countries."

"Scipio!" Augustine sat bolt upright, hanging his legs over the couch. He glared at the old slave. "You know very well," he said, "that the emperor and King Shapur signed their peace treaty months ago. I'm not interested in stale news about silly emperors and kings. Did you hear anything about me? Did you hear that I'd done something . . . something . . . well, surprising?"

"Ah, little master!" Scipio's eyes rolled ceiling-ward in a sad manner. "You are always doing surprising things. So, of course, no one is ever surprised by them."

"I asked you a question, Scipio. Did you hear anything about me this morning?"

Scipio's eyes rolled downward this time. "Woe is me!" he wailed.

"Answer me, Scipio!"

"Well, since you insist. Just before you came for me this noon, one of the other slaves did say something."

"What?"

"He said you slapped the teacher and called him a cockbrain."

"I called him nothing of the sort!"

"You know how rumors are, little master. Exaggerations creep in."

"I told the teacher only a few simple truths." Augustine stared hard at Scipio. "I suppose you've told everyone about this. While you were in the kitchen getting the olive oil, I suppose you told all the other slaves."

"Not all of them, little master. Some of them weren't there."

"*Oh!*" Augustine looked wildly around, seeking some object. The nearest at hand was the small bronze figure of a bird. He grabbed it and hurled it at Scipio. Fortunately the old slave was agile enough when it came to saving his own skin. Then, too, he was used to his child-master's outbursts. He was out of sight and range when the bronze bird landed with a clang on the stone floor of the room.

Augustine leaped from the couch. Muttering under his breath, he pulled a clean tunic over his head. He paced the floor, still muttering. He went to the window and leaned out, gazing at the thickly blooming oleanders in the garden. The intense heat of noontime had gone. The breeze, fresher now, was pleasant on his flushed cheeks.

Calmer, he turned with a sigh and headed for the door. He knew there was only one thing to do. He would go to the atrium where the family gathered before lunch. He would face his parents and hope—hope that the news, having reached the slaves, had not yet reached their ears.

The curtains over the atrium door were closed. Augustine parted them slightly and peeked in. His mother was standing at the far end near the dining room entrance. She was giving instructions in a low voice to one of the serving women.

As in most Roman houses, the atrium was both the family living room and an indoor court. At one end a wide archway, supported by four pillars, gave a broken view of the gardens. Sun poured through an opening in the center of the ceiling. Below the opening was a pool for catching the water when it rained. A fountain splashed in the middle of the pool. Iris blooms and lily pads floated on its shimmering surface. Around it, embedded in a bank of moss, were earthenware pots filled with violets and tropical flowers.

The serving woman glided from the atrium as Augustine stepped in. In the Roman fashion, he addressed his mother by her first name.

"Greetings, Monica."

She turned to him. She was a tall, slender woman with a handsome oval face and dark eyes. One look at them told Augustine that she had heard about his outburst at the teacher. He knew that cool, set look. It was the look she always wore when she was displeased.

Coming across the room, she bent low and kissed him on the forehead. "Greetings, Augustine," she said. "We'll eat as soon as your father joins us."

"Only father?"

"Yes. Navigius and Perpetua are still visiting at your aunt's house." Navigius and Perpetua were Augustine's younger brother and sister.

Monica, leaving him, knelt on one of the sheepskin rugs near the pool. Leaning forward, she began plucking dead leaves from the plants.

Augustine circled the big room aimlessly. Everywhere there were statues: statues of dead Roman emperors; statues of the ancestors of Patricius, Augustine's father.

He seated himself on a bronze stool and studied

his mother's profile. He wished she would say something—shout at him, scold. Anything was better than that cool, set look. Anything! That look hurt worse than all of his teacher's whippings put together.

Suddenly he blurted, "Look here! I don't know what you've heard, but I can tell you this. Some of it isn't true. I did not slap the teacher. I did not call him . . ."

He broke off, checked by a quiet glance from his mother. He hung his head. "You've heard, haven't you?" he asked.

She nodded. "Suppose now," she said, "you begin at the beginning. Tell me exactly what happened."

He had barely started when he broke off again. This time he was stopped by the sound of a familiar voice roaring through the hall. A second later the door curtains were yanked aside. Patricius, Augustine's father, stood in the entranceway.

Patricius was many years older than his wife. When young, he had been a handsome, vigorous man. Lately he had aged fast. There were deep lines in his cheeks. His shoulders sagged. In his youth, his heavy face had been fierce in anger. Now it was merely grumpy, like that of a child in a tantrum.

His pale blue eyes went from Augustine to his wife. "Well, Monica," he said, "you've heard? You know what Augustine did at school this morning?"

Monica nodded. She had not risen from her kneeling position beside the pool.

Patricius went on. "And now," he said, "I assume that Augustine is telling you his story. He's trying to make you believe that it was all the teacher's fault. Even now, I assume, you are dreaming up ways to save him from the whipping he deserves."

"No, Patricius." Monica's voice was low, barely more than a whisper.

"No?" Patricius stared at her in surprise.

"No," she repeated. "Of course Augustine must be punished. But first I think we should hear the details."

"What difference do the details make?" Six long strides carried Patricius across the room. An equal number carried him back.

He lifted his arm, shaking a clenched hand at Augustine. "Young man," he said, "tell me just one thing. Did you or did you not talk back to the teacher this morning?"

Augustine hung his head, biting his lips.

His mother got to her feet. "Your father has asked you a question, Augustine."

Augustine stared at the stone floor. "Yes, father," he said. "I talked back to the teacher."

"Those are all the details I need. Come here, young man. Stand before me."

Augustine did as his father directed. The pale blue eyes burned down on him. "Now listen, Augustine," Patricius went on. "Listen carefully. I want you to realize what you did when you talked back to the teacher. You made a laughing stock of me. A laughing stock of your own father!"

"A laughing stock?"

"Yes, Augustine. You made me look like a fool before the world."

"But how could that be? Nobody knows what happened—nobody, that is, but the students and Scipio and . . ."

He was not allowed to finish. "And everybody else in Tagaste!" his father burst out. "I did not work in the fields this morning, Augustine. I went to the public baths. When I came out an hour ago, who do you think was the first person I met?"

"Who, father?"

"One of the duumvirs, one of the two chief magistrates of the city. And what do you think he did?"

"I have no idea."

"He laughed at me. He told me I was slipping. He said it was a pity that I could no longer make my own son behave!"

Patricius paced again. Back and forth he strode across the sun-flecked room. "By Jupiter!" he exclaimed. "This is the last straw. For years, Augustine, you have gotten away with everything. You disobey me. You disobey your mother. You steal food from the kitchen and wine from the cellar. You do as you please when you please, and somehow you get away with it. But no more! Do you hear—no more!"

He came to a halt beside his wife. "You are a good woman, Monica," he said, inclining his massive head, "and a good mother. You have done a fine job with the other children. But with this one!" He jabbed a quivering forefinger at Augustine. "This one you have spoiled!" he shouted. "You have spoiled him rotten!"

He turned to Augustine. "Go to your room, son," he said. "There will be no lunch for you today. Your mother and I will talk this over. We will decide how severe your punishment should be. Then one of us will come to you."

Augustine's eyes went to his mother. With regret he saw that the cool, set look—the look that spelled displeasure—was still on her handsome face.

"Augustine!" his father roared. "I said *go!*"

Returning to his bedroom, Augustine closed the door curtains. He flung himself on the sleeping couch. He bit the velvet cover in an effort to keep from crying.

He was in for it! Often before when his father had threatened him with a whipping his mother had talked him out of it. It wouldn't be that way this time. This time his mother was as displeased as his father. Even now the two of them were deciding how hard a whipping he should receive.

A sudden breeze wafted into the small room. His eyes went to the window. For a second he was tempted to slip out and run away. He would go and go. Who knows? He might even go as far as Carthage, that great African city on the Mediterranean Sea that people said was almost as gay and beautiful as Rome itself.

Yes! He would stop at Alypius' house. Perhaps Alypius would go with him. They would take some food from Alypius' kitchen . . . Oh, no! Alypius would never steal. He would never do anything to distress his parents. Alypius was such a goody-goody! Besides, if he did agree to go, how would they get to Carthage? They wouldn't even know in which direction to set out.

He turned on his back, staring at the ceiling.

What to do! His mother was always telling him, "When in trouble, pray."

Pray! A good idea! But to whom?

His mother said there was only one God, but his father said there were many gods. There was Jupiter, his father said, and Apollo, and Minerva, and Aesculapius, and dozens of others—so many that his father couldn't remember half their names.

There was only one God, his Christian mother said. There were many, his pagan father said. It was confusing!

His mother said her God did not like little boys to steal and talk back to their elders. His father said his gods were thieves and rascals themselves. So, of course, people who did bad things were only imitating the gods.

Strangely enough, when he, Augustine, did bad things, his pagan father got madder about it than his Christian mother did.

How confusing! How very confusing!

He slipped to his knees beside the couch. He'd try his mother's God and see how he made out. "Dear sweet Jesus"—thus his mother had taught him to begin—"please don't let father give me a whipping, at any rate not a big one."

A light step told him someone had entered the

room. He turned. It was his mother. She stood by the door, a smile in her dark eyes.

"I'm sorry to interrupt you, Augustine," she said. "I hope you have asked God to forgive you."

He started to say that he had asked just that. Then he thought better of it. Lies came easily to Augustine's lips, but not in the presence of his mother. He always had the feeling that she knew when he was not telling the truth.

"Well, not exactly," he confessed. He settled himself on the edge of the couch and dangled his legs. "I sort of asked Him not to let father whip me."

"Oh?" His mother seated herself in the armchair. "Don't you think you should be punished for talking back to the teacher?"

"I suppose so." Augustine's tone made it quite clear that he supposed nothing of the sort. "Only . . ."

"Only?"

"What did I do that was so wrong? I only told the teacher he's a liar, which he is. He's an awful . . . !"

"Augustine!" His mother raised her hand, silencing him. "I don't know whether your teacher is or is not a liar. I only know that in telling him so you committed the sin of detraction."

Detraction? He remembered the bishop at his mother's church using that word. The bishop had explained it. Only, of course, he hadn't listened. The explanation had gone in one ear and out the other. "Detrac-tion?" he faltered.

"Yes, Augustine. To say mean and spiteful things to people or about them is the sin of detraction."

"Even if the things you say about them are true?"

"Even if they are true. The sin of detraction violates our Lord's commandment. He commanded us to love one another."

"But who in the world could love the teacher?"

"Our Lord did not tell us to love only the people who are easy to love. He ordered us to love everybody." Monica smiled. Hers was a quick, pale smile that came and went like the flicker of a candle. "In your next prayer," she went on, "don't ask God to let you out of a punishment you deserve. Ask Him to give you an understanding heart. Ask Him to help you learn to love the teacher."

Augustine glared at the stone floor. There was one thing to be said for his father's pagan gods. They fought among each other. They said mean and spiteful things to each other. There was none of this "I-love-everybody" nonsense among them!

He looked questioningly at his mother. "Well?" he inquired.

"Well what?"

"When do I get my whipping?"

"There will be no whipping."

"No . . . ?" Augustine found it hard to believe his ears. He bounced on the couch. "Then your jolly old God did listen to my prayers after all."

"Augustine!" Monica spoke sharply. "There is one thing you must never do. You must never make silly, stupid jokes about God!"

"I'm sorry." Augustine was sorry—not so much because of what he had said but because there was one thing he couldn't stand. He couldn't stand the look of deep hurt that sometimes came into his mother's eyes—and was in them now. "But how is it that I'm not to be punished?"

"You will be. I suggested a different kind of punishment, and your father has agreed to it."

"A different kind?"

"Yes. Do you know where your teacher lives?"

"In a pigsty."

"Augustine, please!"

"Well, it's true. He can't afford a place in the country. He lives in one of those dirty flats behind the market-place shops. Why do you ask?"

"Because I want you to leave the house early tomorrow morning. Instead of going directly to school, I want you to go first to the home of your teacher."

"To his home? Why?"

"I want you to tell him that you are sorry for what you did this morning."

"Oh, no!" Augustine was on his feet. He looked up at his mother, but his eyes fell at once before the sad look in hers. Young as he was, he understood the meaning of his mother's look. She was just as proud as he was, he realized. The thought of his apologizing to the teacher—or to anyone— made her feel as unhappy as it did him.

He kept his eyes on the floor as she rose. "You will do as I tell you, Augustine," he heard her say. "You will apologize to the teacher." She was silent a second. Then, "You know, Augustine," she said, "your father is right. You are different from your brother and sister. I myself feel that God has marked you. He has marked you for something special. Because of this feeling, I have done a bad thing. As your father says, I have spoiled you."

She moved toward the door. "From now on," she said, "I shall try to be a better mother."

Augustine sat down on the couch, closing his

eyes. When he opened them shortly, his mother was still there.

"Tell me, son," she said, "do you feel that you have learned all you can at the grammar school here?"

"Yes, mother. Why?"

"Your father and I talked about that, too. We decided the time has come for you to attend high school."

"But there is no high school in Tagaste."

"I know. You will have to be sent away."

"Away? To Carthage, perhaps?"

Augustine spoke with such excitement that Monica had to laugh. She did not laugh often, but, when she did, it was a musical and happy sound— so much so that her son found himself laughing with her.

Crossing the room, Monica ran her long fingers affectionately through his curls. "Would you like to go to Carthage?" she asked.

"Oh, yes, mother. People say Carthage is almost the most beautiful place in the world. *Could* I go to school there?"

Monica shook her head. "You are a little young for Carthage. You'll have to go to high school in the city of Madaura."

"Madaura!" Augustine made a face. "Figs!" he

snorted. "I've seen Madaura. It's not a lot bigger than Tagaste."

Monica smiled. "I'll make you a promise," she said. "If you study hard in Madaura, if you behave yourself, then sometime—when you're old enough —we'll send you to one of the big colleges in Carthage. Would you like that?"

"Would I!"

Monica gave her son's curls a gentle tug and left the room. Augustine watched the door curtains shiver into place behind her.

"Oh, joy!" He bounced on the couch, forgetting everything before the prospect of some day going to Carthage, the great and—he was sure— adventure-filled city on the shores of the Mediterranean.

4. The Gang

Augustine studied in Madaura for almost three years. Shortly after his sixteenth birthday he was called home. There he received bad news. Patricius, his father, could no longer afford to keep him in school.

Several things had happened to Patricius. He had become a decurion—that is, a magistrate and a member of the city council of Tagaste. In the Roman empire, the citizens of a city did not support their local public officials. On the contrary, the public officials supported the city. When a man ran for office he had to promise that, if elected, he would pay a large sum of money into the city treasury. In return for this, the citizens had a marble bust made of him and placed on a pedestal in the forum.

Like his son, Patricius was vain. He enjoyed the idea of a likeness of himself standing in the public square where everyone could see it. He ran for office and was elected. But after he had made his payment to the treasury, he had very little money left. To make matters worse, locusts settled on his vineyards and spoiled his grape crop for two seasons running.

Back home, with no classes to attend, Augustine found time heavy on his hands. There was little to do on the farm. His father's slaves did all the real work. All morning he sat in the atrium reading books. In the afternoon he went to the public baths with Patricius.

After the evening meal he called for his friend Alypius. Together they sauntered into town. They spent their evenings on the porch of the public baths with five other teen-age boys who, like themselves, were bored and restless and at loose ends for something to do.

When summer came, one of the boys suggested that they form a gang. Since there were seven of them, they called it "The Seven Against Tagaste." For their motto they invented a bold phrase, "We hate all grownups." Some evenings The Seven Against Tagaste trotted through the market place, stealing small items from the shops. Most evenings they merely sat around, playing cards and talking.

"By all the heroes, I'm weary of this!" Augustine exclaimed one evening, jumping up from the stone bench on the porch of the public baths. Standing in the light of a pine torch attached to the building, he looked around at the others. "What's the matter with us, anyhow?" he demanded. "We call ourselves a gang. A gang is supposed to do exciting things. But what do we do?"

He held up the small object in his hand, a bar of honey he had stolen from one of the food shops.

"This little thing," he snorted, shaking the bar of honey, "will not even be missed. As a gang, we've sworn to annoy all adults. But at this point there isn't an adult in town who knows we even exist. What have we ever done really to call attention to ourselves and make people mad?"

"What do you suggest we do, Augustine?"

The question came from Vinicius—the same Vinicius who, as a towheaded little boy, had been

Augustine's classmate at the Tagaste grammar school. Vinicius spoke with a growl. It was he who had suggested the gang, and so the others had made him their leader.

No longer small and no longer a towhead, Vinicius scowled at Augustine. "I suppose," he said, getting to his feet, "that you don't think I'm a good leader. Maybe you think you'd make a better one."

"Maybe!" Augustine looked at the others again, a half-smile on his lips. "I'll tell you what." He turned back to Vinicius. "I'll challenge you for the leadership. I'll play you a game for it."

"What kind of game?"

"The nut game."

"The nut game?" Vinicius frowned. "Have we ever played that?"

"No. It's a game the men play a lot in the forum. It's easy to learn." Augustine dug three walnut half shells from under the belt of his tunic. "You see," he said, "these are empty." He placed the three shells, open side down, on the bench. Picking up a pebble from the granite porch floor, he placed it under the middle shell.

"Now, Vinicius," he said, "I move these three shells around. When I stop moving them, you try to point to the shell with the pebble under it. If you pick the right shell, you're still leader."

"And if I don't?"

"Why, then, you move the shells, and I try to guess the right one. We go on like that, taking turns, until one of us picks the shell with the pebble under it. Fair enough?"

Again Augustine looked around. His eyes traveled from boy to boy. They came last of all to Alypius.

The years had not changed Alypius much. He had grown only a little. His faintly freckled face was still fresh and open. He grinned at his friend.

"How often have you played this game, Augustine?" he asked.

"Five or six times."

"Do you always win?"

"As a rule."

"How?"

"How?" Augustine looked at Alypius with mock amazement. "I'm lucky, I guess."

"You don't cheat a little, perhaps?"

"I? Cheat? Alypius, you know me better than that."

Alypius laughed. "I know you better than anyone," he said. "That's why I asked."

"I was wondering the same thing." It was Vinicius speaking. "You do cheat, Augustine. I've known you to cheat at games."

"Oh, I cheat a little at cards for the fun of it."

Augustine shrugged. "But the nut game is different. There's no way in the world one could cheat at it. What do you say, fellows?" He turned to the others. "All in favor of our playing the nut game for the leadership, raise your hands."

Five hands fluttered in the air. The game was on.

"I'll move the shells first," Augustine told Vinicius. "That way, you get first crack at the leadership."

He lifted the middle shell to show that the pebble was under it. Then swiftly he slid the shells about, talking all the time and making such strange faces that all the others roared with laughter.

All, that is, except Alypius. He didn't watch his friend's face. He watched his hands. He was the only one who saw Augustine hastily run one hand over his stolen bar of honey—so that when he started moving the shells, the pebble stuck between two of his fingers! As a result, there was no way that Vinicius could pick the shell with the pebble under it—because the pebble wasn't under any of the shells!

Glancing quickly to the side, Augustine saw that Alypius had spotted his trick. He didn't worry, however. Alypius, he knew, was the most loyal friend a person could have. He wouldn't tell on him.

When it was Vinicius' turn to move the shells, Augustine scooped up a new pebble, when Vinicius wasn't looking, and slipped it under a shell. Of course, Augustine won the game, for all he had to do was pick up one of the shells, and, if the new pebble were not there, drop the one he had stuck between his fingers. As Augustine lifted the shell and dropped the pebble at the same time, it looked as if the pebble had been underneath the shell and had fallen out as he lifted it. Augustine had won, and a cheer rang through the porch. The boys knew that he was a cheat and a liar, and that he had a dreadful temper. They also knew that he had imagination. Breathlessly, now that he was their leader, they waited to hear what daring adventure he would suggest to them.

First of all, the new commander of The Seven Against Tagaste held out his hand to the man he had deposed.

"Are you going to be a good sport about it, Vinicius?" he asked.

What choice did Vinicius have? He shook Augustine's hand and grinned.

Then Augustine jumped onto the bench and motioned the others to come close. They formed an eager semicircle in front of him.

"All right, boys," he said, "I'll tell you what

we're going to do tonight. Do all of you know the farm of old Tullus about a half mile from the city gates?"

"Tullus? Tullus?" The name passed from mouth to mouth.

"He's a poor old man who lives by himself," Augustine told them. "And do you know how he makes his living? He has a little pear orchard." Augustine dropped his voice to a dramatic whisper. "And tonight, fellows," he went on, "we're going to do something that people in this town will talk about for months to come. We're going to strip every pear off old Tullus' trees so that when fall comes he won't have a thing to sell!"

Another cheer. Only Alypius frowned and was silent. Augustine's eyes were on him. "I know how it is with you," he said. "I've watched you in the market place. The other boys steal, but you never do. Well, I'm leader now, and I make the rules. Any boy who's afraid to steal can get out of the gang this minute."

Augustine leaped from the bench. "All right!" he shouted. "Follow me."

They followed, charging into the street like escaping steam. Only Alypius hung back a few seconds, shaking his head sadly. Finally, with a sigh, he ran after them.

Half an hour later they were in Tullus' orchard, shouting and laughing and knocking the green fruit from the trees. Some of the boys stored pears under their tunics, although Augustine kept telling them that they were hard as rocks at this season and no good to eat. Vinicius tried one anyhow and brought a fresh roar of laughter when he spat it out with a howl of disgust.

"What are we going to do with all these pears?" he cried, leaning back so that the fruit under his tunic made a comical mound.

"Do with them?" Augustine thought fast. "I know!" he yelled. "There's another old farmer down the road here. He keeps pigs. We'll feed the pears to the pigs!"

They raced down the road, still shouting, still laughing. Reaching the pigsty, they pelted the startled and grunting animals. Their barrage was barely under way when a door of the nearby farmhouse opened and an old man appeared, looking like a ghost in his long white nightgown. They could see his mouth, wide open as a cave, in the wavering light of his torch.

"Drop your pears, gang!" Augustine shouted. "Scatter and run for it!"

He himself kept one pear. Taking quick aim, he hurled it with all his strength. His throw was good.

The pear caught the oncoming farmer full in the stomach. Dazed, the old man fell forward, torch and all, his face squishing in the mud of the pigsty.

Augustine ran. He knew a short cut around the hill, through the valley, and up another low hill to his father's farm. Looking ahead, he saw that Alypius had thought of the short cut too. Stronger and longer-limbed, Augustine soon passed his friend. He kept on until, out of breath, his insides sore from laughing, he could run no farther.

He flung himself down in the grass, heavy with dew. Seconds later, Alypius came into view and flung himself down beside him. For a time they lay there, getting their breath, unable to speak.

Presently Augustine sat up. He was suddenly aware of the night around him, of the crickets singing in the grass, of a tree toad trilling somewhere, of an indigo sky spattered with distant stars. He felt a scratchy feeling in his throat. With sudden alarm, he realized that he was about to cry. Indeed, a single sob escaped him. Only with difficulty, glancing at Alypius, did he turn it into what he hoped sounded like a cough.

The night sounds again. Then Alypius spoke.

"What's the matter, Augustine?"

"Matter? Nothing is the matter. It was a great night."

"Was it, Augustine?"

Augustine's head dropped. "Oh, Alypius," he said, "what is the matter with me? Why do I do such silly, pointless things? Why did I make myself leader of the gang? I don't really care about it at all. Why did I drag the boys out here to steal that poor man's pears? The pears are no good, and the old man never did us any harm. Even if he did, it was all so silly, so pointless."

Augustine did not look at his friend as he spoke. Nor did he turn when Alypius spoke to him in his gentle voice.

"You've had a tough time of it lately, haven't you, Augustine?"

Augustine nodded. "It's awful," he admitted, "having nothing to do. If only I could go to Carthage the way mother said I could years ago. But there's no chance of that now. Father can't afford it." He tore a blade of grass from the earth and ran it through his fingers. "It's worst of all at home," he went on. "All I do is sit around and read. And try to keep out of my mother's way."

"Why do you avoid your mother?"

"You know why." Augustine uttered an odd sound, half laugh and half grunt. "Because she's always after me to become a Catholic Christian. That's why. She doesn't say it right out very often.

But I know what's on her mind. She stares at me and she prays."

"Do you think you ever will become a Christian?"

"Who knows?" Augustine shrugged. "Funny thing. Right before I went to Madaura, I thought maybe I would. Just to please my mother, you understand. But while I was in Madaura, I don't know. I met so many people. I heard about so many different religions. Pretty soon I didn't know what to think. Sometimes . . ." He fell silent.

"Sometimes," Alypius prodded him.

"Sometimes I wish I'd been brought up in a different kind of home."

"What do you mean?"

"You know. It's confusing having parents who belong to different religions."

"But I hear that your father is taking instructions from the bishop."

"Now he is, yes. Mother has finally persuaded him to become a catechumen. That's a person who's studying to become a Catholic, you know." Again Augustine uttered an odd little sound—a laugh with an edge on it. "But when I was little, father couldn't see mother's religion at all. He was a pagan, she a Christian. He pulled me one way. She pulled me another."

Augustine wadded up the blade of grass in his

hand and tossed it aside. "I'll tell you something, Alypius. I'll tell you what bothers me about Christianity." He was silent again.

"Go on," Alypius urged him. "What does bother you about it?"

"Mother says God created the world and that everything God does is good. But look at what we did tonight. We robbed the poor farmer's orchard for no reason—just for the sake of doing something evil. Now I ask you: if everything God does is good, why is there so much evil in His world?" Augustine sighed. "When I find the answer to that question," he declared, "I'll know what to believe!"

"You'll find the answer some day."

"I hope so." Augustine got to his feet. "Come along," he said. "It's well after midnight."

They trudged through the starlit night in silence and parted company at Augustine's place. Once in the garden at the foot of the front steps, Augustine was startled to see a light in the atrium. Going to one of the windows and standing on his toes, he looked in.

The light came from a bed of coals burning in a basin on an iron tripod. At first Augustine thought his mother was alone in the room. Then he saw that she had company.

There was something familiar about the big man

sitting near the fountain in the center of the atrium. Augustine remembered seeing him in the house on previous occasions. But when? He was not certain. Nor could he recall the man's name.

His mother and her guest were deep in conversation. They broke off as he stepped in. Looking up, his mother gave him one of her pale, flickering smiles. The big man jumped to his feet with a bounce.

"By the shades of my ancestors!" he exclaimed, his voice filling the room. "Here is the lost sheep himself."

He bore down on Augustine, clasping his hand with such force that Augustine's fingers ached.

"I don't suppose you remember me," he cried. "I haven't been in this house for years—too many years, alas. I am Romanianus."

Augustine remembered now. Romanianus was one of his parents' oldest friends. He was a wealthy merchant who lived on a large estate near Alypius' house, but he spent much of his time in Carthage where he ran one of North Africa's biggest wine shops.

"Greetings, sir," Augustine said. "I am happy to see you again."

Over Romanianus' shoulder he could see that his

mother had risen. "I've been telling Romanianus all about you, son," she said.

Augustine waited till she had resumed her seat and Romanianus had returned to his. Then, planting himself on the bronze footstool near the big man's chair, he grinned at his mother.

"I know you've been telling Romanianus the truth about me, mother," he said, "seeing that he calls me the lost sheep."

Romanianus laughed. Like everything else about him, his laugh was big and hearty. "Lost sheep, found sheep, black sheep, white sheep!" he shouted. "Who cares? Only your mother, Augustine, worries about things like that." He bent across the arm of his chair, dropping his big hand with a thump on Augustine's knee. "Tell me, my boy," he said with a broad wink, "has she pulled you in yet?"

"Into what, sir?"

"Into the Catholic Church, of course. She's about to bring in your father, and she's been working on me for years. Don't tell me she hasn't been working on you."

"Oh, yes, sir. Only . . ." Augustine lowered his eyes, feeling suddenly uncomfortable. "Only I guess I'm a pretty hard nut to crack."

"She'll get you!" Romanianus gave Augustine's

knee another pounding and withdrew his hand. "She'll get you!" he roared. "Your mother doesn't make much noise in this world, but watch out. Sooner or later she gets whatever she's after."

The big man turned to Augustine's mother, favoring her with an enormous smile. "Well, Monica," he said, "are you going to tell the boy now?"

"Tell me?" Augustine looked questioningly at his mother. "Tell me what?"

Monica's pale smile came and went. "You are going to Carthage, son," she said.

To Carthage! The very word sent a thrill deep down into Augustine. "To school?" he inquired.

Monica nodded. "Your father and I have been worried about you," she said. "You have been so restless since you came home. So tonight I asked Romanianus over. He understands. He has offered us enough money to send you to school in Carthage."

"Oh, mother!" Augustine half rose from his stool and sat down again. Then, jumping up, he stood by Romanianus' chair. "Sir, I don't know how to thank you."

"Don't!" Romanianus rose. He brought down both hands, with bruising force, on Augustine's shoulders. "Your mother and father have given me their devoted friendship for many years, Augustine. In helping you, I am only paying them back. Besides . . ." He gave Augustine a sly wink and glanced sideways at his mother. "I hear that, though you are a lost sheep, you are a good student. Your father tells me that some day you will be a great orator."

"I don't know about that, sir."

"We shall see." Romanianus gave Augustine a friendly shake. "I tell you what. I have a son twelve years old. Perhaps after you've finished your schooling you can come back here and tutor him for a while."

"I'll do that, sir. It's a promise."

"Fine! Can you be ready to leave by the first of the week?"

"Oh, sir, I could be ready to leave for Carthage yesterday."

Romanianus laughed. Crossing the room he gave his hand to Monica. "I must go now," he said. "Remember me to your good husband. Tell him the next time I come not to yawn himself off to bed at such an early hour."

Augustine, lost in dreams, did not hear his mother the first time she addressed him. She spoke a second time. "Augustine."

"Oh, yes, mother."

"Romanianus' horse is at the rear of the house."

"I'll get it for him."

When Augustine brought the horse around, his mother and Romanianus were already at the front gate. The big man gave him another friendly blow on the shoulder and swung himself up.

When he had gone, Augustine turned a smiling face to his mother. Lately—ever since his return from Madaura, in fact—he had felt a little shy and ill at ease when he was alone with her. His only feeling tonight was one of pleasure—pleasure at the thought of going to school in Carthage.

"Happy?" his mother asked.

"I give you a promise," he told her. "I'll study hard. Maybe, as father says, I shall be a great orator."

"Maybe." Monica smiled. "You know, of course, there's only one thing I want you to be."

"I know, mother. I'll think about that, too. Well . . ."

Monica nodded. "Yes, you must get some sleep. We have busy days ahead getting you packed and ready."

He ran into the atrium. Halfway across the room something—he knew not what—prompted him to stop and turn around. His mother was still standing by the gate. In the light streaming from the house he saw that her head was bowed, her lips moving. She was praying, he knew, praying once again for his conversion. He sighed, shook his head, and hurried down the long hall toward his room.

5. In the City of the Many-Headed Goddess

In Augustine's time people spoke of Carthage as Roman Carthage because it belonged to the Romans and had been built by them. It was the second city of Carthage to stand on the sandy peninsula where centuries later would stand the city of Tunis in the country of Algeria.

The first Carthage (Phoenician Carthage as it

came to be known) was founded almost nine hundred years before the birth of Christ. It belonged to the people of Phoenicia, an Asiatic country later called Lebanon, only a day's journey or so from the little town of Nazareth where our Lord grew up.

In the ninth century before Christ the Phoenicians were great merchants and sailors. Their oar-driven galleys roamed the Mediterranean Sea. Putting in at ports along the coast, the Phoenicians sold the rich products of the Orient to the people of southern Europe and North Africa.

Often, in their wanderings, the Phoenician merchant-sailors noticed the big North African peninsula just southwest of the island of Sicily. They called it the Wonderful Peninsula.

"What a place it would be for a city," they told one another. "It would not be hard to build safe harbors for our ships there."

In time, word of the Wonderful Peninsula reached the ears of Princess Dido, sister of the Phoenician king. Dido was a beautiful young woman and an ambitious one. She liked the idea of founding a colony for her country in distant North Africa. One evening, in the year 850 B.C., she boarded a long galley in the harbor of Tyre, the capital city of Phoenicia, and sailed into the setting sun.

Arriving at the Wonderful Peninsula, Princess Dido was pleased with what she saw. She pointed to a sandstone hill rising 200 feet into the sky not far from the shore.

"We will put our fort there," she said, "and build the rest of the town on the slopes of the hill and in the valley around it."

It was so done. Princess Dido called her city Kart Hadasht, meaning New Town. But the weather is warm in North Africa. Soon the people found it easier to run the words "Kart" and "Hadasht" together and call their town simply Carthage.

Carthage grew apace. In time it became one of the great cities of the world with a population of 700,000. In time, too, the Phoenicians became the rulers of almost all North Africa.

By the third century before Christ, the rulers of Rome, on the far side of the Mediterranean, were pulling at their togas and muttering among themselves.

"This is not good," they said. "Soon the Phoenicians of Carthage will get too big for themselves. They will come across the sea and conquer us."

So the Roman rulers did what silly and frightened rulers have done since the world began. To keep Carthage from conquering them—which Carthage had no intention of doing—they built huge armies and many ships with the idea of conquering Carthage.

It took them three long series of bloody wars to do it. History would call them the Punic Wars because the Romans spoke of the Phoenicians of Carthage as the Poeni or Punic people. Finally, in 146 B.C., a Roman force under General Scipio Africanus Minor invaded Carthage. Smashing up the hill and into the fort, the Romans set the city on fire.

For seventeen days it burned. When the smoke cleared, Phoenician Carthage had been wiped from the face of the earth!

After that, Rome ruled North Africa. In the last century before Christ, in the days of Julius Caesar, the Romans built a new Carthage on the site of the old. Like Phoenician Carthage before it, Roman Carthage grew fast. Before long it, too, was one of the great cities of the world. And so it remained until the year 698 when an Arab army, charging in from the East, once again wiped the city of Carthage from the face of the earth.

Augustine was sixteen years old, almost seventeen, when, in the fall of the year 370, he arrived in Carthage for the first time. He had more company on the trip than he had expected. At the last minute his friend Alypius, after many talks with his parents, had decided to come along and enter school with him.

Romanianus had rented lodgings for them on a winding alley known as the Street of the Jewelers. His silver coach stopped before the stone stair which climbed the wall of a food shop to what, for a time, would be the boys' second-floor home.

As soon as the coach stopped, all was bustle and noise. Romanianus' slaves carried the boys' luggage up the white steps. Romanianus himself rushed after them. He raced through the rooms of the flat, making sure that all was in readiness for his young charges. His big voice filled the place, warming it like a fire.

He shouted orders at the slaves. He shouted advice at the boys. "Be careful of pickpockets on the streets," he roared at them. "You're not in the little country town of Tagaste now. You're in the great city of Carthage."

"As if we didn't know," Augustine whispered to Alypius with a wink.

"And whatever you do," Romanianus bellowed, "stay away from the theaters. The shows on the stages of Carthage are not for decent eyes to behold."

"We'll go to the theater the first chance we get,"

Augustine assured Alypius behind a shielding hand.

"And last, but not least," Romanianus prefaced his parting words, "keep out of the wine shops. After all, I'm responsible for you boys. I know Augustine is a lost sheep already, but I don't want to send him back to his mother any more lost than he is."

The minute Romanianus departed, Augustine jumped almost as high as the ceiling. "Alypius!" he shouted. "We're free! We're free!"

"But, Augustine, we were free as anyone could want to be back in Tagaste."

"Oh, no, Alypius. Back home we were tied to our mothers' apron strings. Now we can go where we please, do what we please, think what we please. Come!" He kicked the canvas bag holding his clothes into a corner of the largest of the three rooms. "Let us explore the city!"

"But, Augustine, we must unpack first."

"Unpack! We can unpack any old time. Let's see the great city now."

"But, Augustine . . ." Alypius was a neat little fellow. He was horrified at the thought of leaving their new home without first putting it in order. But Augustine was already gone. Reluctantly, Alypius went after him.

Down below they encountered such movement and color as neither of them had ever hoped to see. The Street of the Jewelers wound like a narrow canyon between six-story buildings faced with thickly pebbled mortar.

There were shops, and shops, and more shops. Across the front of each open stall, by way of a counter, was a granite slab. There were no doors. The merchants, coming and going, ducked under the slabs. On counter after counter twinkled ornaments of all sorts for, true to its name, the street was mostly jewelry stores.

Augustine walked so fast and looked so hard that he had to admit afterwards he saw very little that afternoon. It was all a thrilling and magnificent whirl.

Most thrilling were the people. He could see by their garments that they came from all corners of the earth. Swarthy Arabs plodded by in their tent-like cloaks and pointed hoods. Richly curtained litters glided above their heads. Some, resting on long poles, were carried by Numidian slaves. Some swayed between the humps of camels or on the broad backs of elephants. Stately Moors, dark and handsome, raced through the crowd as though in seven-league boots.

The boys walked north, away from the sea.

Shortly they were in the forum, a mammoth paved square almost completely surrounded by public buildings. Their marble walls, in the setting sun, gave off every color of the rainbow, tinting the very air. Almost the largest of them, Augustine noted, was the Catholic basilica.

But what seized the boys' attention was the sight overhead. They were looking up at the fort—the citadel, as people called it. It stood on the high hill named the Byrsa, the hill that had so entranced the beautiful Princess Dido more than a thousand years before. At the far end of the forum, sweeping straight up the hill to the citadel, was a broad flight of steps.

There were sixty steps in all. The boys ran all the way. Reaching the top, the view that spread before them took away what little breath they had left.

Here was another mammoth square and many more buildings. Dominating the area was by far the tallest building either boy had ever seen. It rose into the sky in tiers, like one of the pyramids. Soaring from the top tier was a statue taller than the building itself. It was the statue of a woman. Held high in her right hand was an enormous ornament shaped like a crescent moon. Crescent and woman were made of yellow gold. They shone in the level rays of the sun with a blinding luster.

Alypius seized his friend's arm. "What? Who?" he demanded.

Augustine was amused at the startled expression on Alypius' face. "Romanianus told us about that statue on the trip here," he said. "But I remember now. You slept most of the journey. That's Tanit."

"Tanit?"

"The moon goddess. Many people here are pagans. Tanit is their favorite deity. Some call her the many-headed goddess."

"But the statue has only one head."

"Oh, that's not the real statue. The real one's inside the temple. Come along. We'll look at it."

There were people coming and going through the pillared entryways of the big temple. Inside the boys halted, abashed, for the shadowy interior was vast. Its travertine walls rose up and up. They had to lean their heads far back to see the splendid mosaics of the ceiling. Bringing his head forward and straining to see into the distance, Alypius gasped. "Look!" he whispered.

Augustine was already looking. On a low platform at the far end of the huge room sat the moon goddess. The statue on the temple roof was a thing of beauty. But this squatting monster of many hands and many heads was ugly and horrifying beyond belief. Every one of its twelve heads was a nightmare in bronze. In every face the huge and ghastly mouth was wide open as though demanding to be fed.

Alypius sniffed the air. "Augustine!" He was still speaking in a whisper. "Is there a fire? I smell smoke."

"Naturally you smell smoke."

"Naturally?"

"There's a blazing furnace inside the goddess. The people throw things down her throats as sacrifices to her."

"What do they throw into the furnace? Goats?"

"Goats indeed! Babies."

"*Human* babies?"

"Of course."

"Oh, no! You're joking. Say it isn't so. Say it isn't so this minute or I'll be sick. I'll be sick on the spot!"

Augustine bent double with silent laughter. He, too, spoke in a whisper. "I'll tell you the truth, Alypius. In the old days they did sacrifice babies to the goddess. They did so until the Christians came along and forced them to stop. Thanks to them, there's a law against it now."

Augustine grinned, seeing the growing look of horror on his friend's face. "I'm telling you the truth," he said. "In the old days, if parents didn't want to be bothered with one of their babies, they threw it to the goddess. No one could blame them for it. After all, they were doing it for religious reasons. Sometimes . . ."

But Augustine saw there was no use going on. Alypius had fled. Turning and standing on his toes, Augustine could see his friend zigzagging through the crowd, heading for the fresh air of the open square.

He followed quickly—and willingly. The ugly goddess and the foul atmosphere of the place had turned his stomach a little, too.

Early the next morning Romanianus took the boys to the School of Rhetoric, as Carthage's college of oratory and law was called. Augustine was delighted to be a student again. For all his love of fun, he wanted to make something of himself. All his life his father had predicted that Augustine would some day be a great orator. He himself dreamed of the day when he would stand on a rostrum, one of those platforms that stood in the forum of every Roman city, spellbinding crowds of people with his speech making.

He studied hard, and the days passed quickly and pleasantly. Alypius was less happy at first. For a long time he was homesick.

One afternoon he came into the flat humming to himself. Looking up from his studies, Augustine was pleased to see a smile once more on his friend's face. "Well," he said, "you look more like yourself. Anything good happen?"

"Did it!" Even Alypius' voice was back to normal—chirpy and bubbly. "I was in one of the other classes today and guess what?"

"I'll guess. What?"

"I met a boy we used to go to school with years ago in Tagaste."

"No!"

"Yes. I invited him to supper."

"Well, now, we'd better get in some food."

"He's at the shop now, buying stuff for us. He insisted on doing it. I couldn't stop him."

There was a knock at the door. "Our guest?" Augustine inquired. Alypius nodded. He had not mentioned the guest's name, and Augustine did not immediately recognize the handsome young man who stepped in as Alypius opened the door. He was a tall boy with the dark and striking features of a Moor. Alypius relieved him of his packages and pulled him into the room.

"You remember Augustine, of course," he said.

The newcomer took Augustine's hand. "Oh, yes," he said without smiling. "You haven't changed a bit."

Augustine frowned. He was of the opinion that

he had changed a great deal. He liked to think that, during his six months in Carthage, he had shed his country looks and manners. At seventeen he thought of himself as a full-fledged man, wise and worldly.

"I'm sorry," he said, "but . . ."

"You don't remember me. Well, I won't keep you guessing. I am Harmodius."

"Harmodius?" The name rang a bell for Augustine, but only a distant one.

"In Tagaste the boys always called me the Moor, as I was the only one in the class."

"Oh, yes, of course. Harmodius, the Moor!" Augustine pumped the tall boy's hand vigorously. "May all the heroes strike me for a dullard. Sit down, Harmodius. It's good to see you again."

Harmodius seated himself. He sat stiffly upright, and Augustine wondered if he ever smiled. He had a sullen look, but, as the evening wore on and the boys talked of old times, Augustine saw that Harmodius' expression was deceiving. He had wit and humor. Every now and then, without smiling or otherwise altering his expression, he would send his hosts into gales of laughter with a sudden droll remark.

He was intelligent, too, and learned. Augustine soon discovered that Harmodius had read more of the old Greek and Roman works than he had. Before the evening was over, he had made up his mind that Harmodius would be a good friend to have.

After that the three boys spent their spare time together. Harmodius lived down the street. On school nights he brought his books and studied with the two friends. On week-end nights the three of them roamed the city together.

One of their favorite haunts was the Carthage waterfront. There were two harbors—two huge, man-made basins. The inner basin was the military harbor. It was a perfect circle ringed by 222 docks, each large enough to hold a Roman warship. A canal linked it to the merchants' harbor, an even larger basin to the south.

In the early evening the park along the waterfront was like a carnival. People strolled, laughing and talking, along the portico-covered paths. A crowd circled the high platform where dancing girls performed to the haunting strains of Egyptian sistra and Grecian lutes.

Standing with his friends, watching the dancers one evening, Augustine's eyes fell on a girl some twenty feet away. She was young—about his own age or less, he guessed. She wore a blue tunic trimmed with red, a single hibiscus in her dark hair. At first he did not think of her as especially pretty. But when he turned away, the image of her rounded profile remained stamped on his mind.

He looked again. This time he decided that he had never seen a lovelier human being. Just then the girl moved away, heading in the direction of the broad street which cut the park in two.

Augustine acted on impulse. "Excuse me, gentlemen," he said, leaving his two friends. He heard them shouting after him, asking where he thought he was going. But he had no ears for their questions.

At this hour the street traffic was heavy. The girl had to stop a moment at the curb, and Augustine caught up with her.

Augustine was nothing if not bold. He was fully aware of his own charm and good looks. Never had he doubted that a person, meeting him for the first time, would take to him. Reaching the girl's side, he began speaking immediately.

"My name is Augustine," he said. "What's yours? Tell me at once, or I'll go to the military harbor this very minute and drown myself!"

His boldness, his breathlessness—and above all his comic threat—were too much for the girl. She laughed. "My name is Melania," she said.

"Melania!" Her laugh was music, Augustine

had decided; and her name was music! He was about to speak again when he realized that Melania had left him. The traffic had thinned, and she was hastily crossing the street.

He ran after her. On the far side he lost sight of her in the crowd. He pushed through, bumping into people, muttering apologies, laughing in their faces when they scolded at him. He pushed this way, that way. Then he saw her again. She was entering one of the three streets leading to the forum.

He sprinted. Catching up with her, he took no chances. He seized her arm.

"Melania," he said, "where are you going?"

She turned to him, fire in her large eyes. "What business is that of yours?"

"Ah, Melania! As of five minutes ago everything about you became my business. Tell me, please. Where are you going?"

"I am going home if you must know."

"Alone and at this hour? In a city full of footpads and other criminals? Oh, no. Let me go with you. Let me be your strong right arm."

"I have a very good right arm of my own, thank you!" Melania snapped, pulling loose the arm he was holding and hurrying away.

He came even with her again. This time he

seized her hands, turning her so that they were face to face.

Most Carthaginian women painted their faces heavily and sprinkled gold dust in their hair. Not Melania. She wore no paint, no gold dust. Her eyes were green and round as disks. Her skin, it seemed to Augustine, was cleaner and whiter than ivory.

"Please!" Augustine put on the saddest of tones. "If you do not let me see you home, I shall drown myself first in the military harbor and then in the merchants' harbor. Think of the fix you'll be in. You'll have my death on your conscience not only once but twice."

She laughed again. "But we're strangers," she protested.

"Five minutes will remedy that." He slid his arm through hers. "Tell me about yourself. Tell me your whole life. Begin at the beginning."

She told him as they walked along. The streets were quiet. They found only a few people strolling in the moonlit forum.

Melania, he learned, had been born and brought up in a country town not far from Carthage.

"And when did you come to the city?" he inquired.

"Right after I was given my freedom."

"You were born a slave?"

The girl nodded. "But I had a very kind master," she said. "After father died a few years ago, he gave mother and me our freedom. He even gave us some money so we could set ourselves up in Carthage."

"And what do you do?"

"Oh, mother owns a stall in the market place. I help her. I weave baskets from palm leaves, and we sell them."

They walked in silence for a while. Augustine could hear the gentle flip-flop of the girl's sandals on the forum pavement.

"Tell me more, Melania," he begged.

"There's not much else except . . ."

"Except?"

"I'm a catechumen."

When Augustine was silent she gave him a probing look. "Perhaps," she said, "you do not know what that is. A catechumen is a person who is taking instructions to become a Catholic Christian."

"I know, Melania. My mother is one."

"A catechumen?"

"No. A Catholic."

"And you?"

Augustine shrugged. "Oh, me," he said, "I have no religion."

"But you must have!"

"Why?"

"One must believe in something. Otherwise life is meaningless."

"Oh, I have my beliefs."

"What are they?"

He halted. "Funny you should ask that question here," he said. "Everything I believe is written on a table here in the forum. Come." He led her to one of the stone card tables standing alongside the forum sidewalks. "There," he said, pointing to some Latin words carved into the table top. "Read them. There's moonlight enough. Read them aloud."

She bent over the table. "To hunt," she read, "to bathe, to gamble, to laugh: this is living."

She looked up at Augustine. "This is your philosophy?" she asked. He nodded. "I'll tell you something." Melania smiled. "You are the biggest liar I ever met."

"Why, Melania! When you know me better you'll realize I never tell lies."

"Oh, yes, you do. The biggest is the one you tell yourself."

"And what is that?"

"That you believe this!" Her hand swept the air above the words inscribed in the table. "You know there's more to life than hunting and bathing and whatever else it says. Have you any idea what you are, Augustine?"

"It's a wise man who knows what he is."

"You're a searcher!"

"Am I?"

"Yes." She let him take her arm again as they walked on. "You'll suffer a lot before you find what you're looking for. But don't despair. You'll find it."

"What am I looking for, Melania?"

"The truth, Augustine."

They had entered a narrow side street, dark under a series of stone arches linking the tall buildings on either side. Melania stopped before a door set deep in a cement wall.

"This is where I live," she said.

"But we've only just started talking. May I come in for a while?"

She shook her head. "Mother and I have only one room, and she's old. She needs her sleep."

"But, Melania . . ." He felt her hand slip into his. It was as cool as spring water. He bent toward her, speaking fast. "Melania, I'm a student at the rhetoric school, but I'm free at nightfall. May I come for you tomorrow night, and the night after that, and the night after that? I'm not rich. I can't take you to the theater or the music hall. But at least we could walk and talk and . . ." He broke off, aware that he was crushing and hurting her small hand.

He released it. "May I see you tomorrow night?" he pleaded.

"Yes." She spoke so low that he only just heard her.

Then she was gone. He was alone and, for the first time in his life, lonely. He felt as if every other human being had departed from the world.

Then he remembered! She had said yes—yes, she would see him tomorrow night. With a leap he took off, running down the narrow street in the direction of the forum, shouting as he ran.

Now a new life began for Augustine. Alypius and Harmodius saw no more of him in the evenings. They teased him, of course. They made all the jokes that young men, since time began, have made about a friend in love.

Arriving home late one evening, Augustine found his friends busy with their schoolbooks. He burst into the flat. Augustine never entered a place —he crashed in. He was almost as noisy a person as Romanianus. He had a rich, full voice and a hearty laugh.

Tonight he was not even smiling. His friends looked up from their desks as he came in. They exchanged glances.

"And did our great lover have a pleasant evening?" Harmodius inquired in a voice like a damaged bassoon. "And is his Melania still more beautiful than the moon?"

"And are her eyes," Alypius chimed in, "still brighter than all the stars?"

"Oh, be still, both of you!" Augustine planted himself on the stool between the two desks. He leaned toward Alypius. "Look here," he said, "you're studying to be a lawyer. What is the Roman law about marriage? Can I marry a freedwoman, a woman who was born a slave?"

"Marriage!" Alypius' eyes opened wide.

Harmodius released his breath in an over-long sigh. "Thus was it always," he singsonged. "When a man of sense falls in love, a fool is born."

"Marriage!" Alypius repeated in a mutter. "You're not thinking of marrying Melania, Augustine?"

"Don't ask silly questions. Answer mine. What is the law?"

"The law says you cannot marry a freedwoman."

"Oh, no!" Leaping up, Augustine paced the floor. "Oh, no!" he moaned. Stopping at the window, he leaned his flushed face into the soft breeze outside.

Alypius joined him. "Are you serious about this?" he asked.

Augustine nodded.

"And have you asked Melania?"

"Yes."

"And?"

"She has accepted me."

Alypius glanced at Harmodius, who was watching them with curious eyes. He turned back to Augustine. "Cheer up then," he said. "Half of the men in Carthage are married to women who used to be slaves."

"What are you saying?" Augustine grabbed his friend's shoulders, shaking him hard. "First you tell me I can't marry Melania. Now you tell me I can."

Alypius smiled. "Roman law says you cannot marry her in a legal way. Roman custom, however, says the two of you may join hands, promise to love, honor, and obey, and so become man and wife. It's called a common-law marriage."

"Common-law?" Augustine frowned. "Is that a good sort of marriage?"

Alypius nodded.

"You're sure?" Augustine persisted. "Melania would not consent to anything except a good sort of marriage. You're absolutely sure?"

"I'm sure, Augustine. There's only one problem."

"Yes?"

"Your mother. She would never approve of a marriage made outside of the Church."

Augustine withdrew his hands from Alypius' shoulders. "I've thought about that," he said. He paced the room again, returning to the window. "But what my mother doesn't know," he said firmly, "won't hurt her."

"You mean to keep it a secret from her?"

"I do."

"But Romanianus . . ."

"What about him?"

"It takes money to support a wife, Augustine. Where else can you get money except from him? He'll have to know, and he's bound to tell your mother."

"We'll see about that." Augustine crossed the room to the hall door.

Harmodius rose. "And where do you think you're going at this late hour?" he demanded. He received no reply, for Augustine had already left the flat.

It was an hour's walk to Romanianus' townhouse. The big villa was dark when Augustine arrived. He aroused the slaves. They, in turn, aroused their master and lighted the coal lamps in the richly furnished atrium.

When Romanianus appeared, grumpy and

groggy with sleep, there was a stormy scene. He would not hear of what Augustine wished to do. "No, no, no!" he shouted. "I will not agree to a marriage unless it is made with your mother's knowledge and consent." He walked away from Augustine, shaking with anger.

Augustine followed his retreating back with his eyes. "Stay where you are," he said. "I'll be with you again shortly."

He was gone before the big man could ask him what he had in mind. When he returned, all of an hour and a half later, Melania was at his side.

One look at the slender girl with the green eyes and the high, serene brow, and Romanianus' whole manner changed. He took her hand and gazed at her face for a long time.

Augustine smiled to himself. He realized that Romanianus was seeing what everyone saw in Melania—the goodness and honesty that shone from her eyes.

"But I understand you are a catechumen," the big merchant said to her, his voice quiet for a change. "I gather you believe as the Catholics do?"

Melania nodded.

"But you would take this boy anyhow? Even though it means a marriage that will keep you from entering the Church?"

Melania spoke in a very low voice. "I would give up anything for Augustine," she said.

Romanianus sighed. He turned to Augustine. "Very well," he said.

"I have your promise then?" Augustine asked eagerly. "You will not tell mother?"

Romanianus nodded. "It shall be our secret," he said. "Frankly, I would marry this girl myself if I were young and free to do so."

Augustine laughed gaily. "She wouldn't have you!" he cried.

"She would be getting a better husband if she did!" Romanianus gave the young man a sharp look. "You are getting a jewel," he said. "As for you . . ." He turned to Melania. "You have my sympathy. You are marrying a boy who is at once a lost sheep and a raging lion. He will try your patience, Melania. Oh, my child, how he will try your patience!"

6. Enter the Prince of Darkness

And so they were married. And so they went to live in a first-floor apartment which Romanianus found and furnished for them at the rear of a building on the Street of the Jewelers.

There were two small rooms and a garden with a fountain under a spread of myrtle bushes. Melania dusted her little house and cleaned it as though it were a palace. She was a good housekeeper. In the mornings she rose early and made their breakfast on a fire in the hearth. All day they were apart, she at her mother's shop, he at school. At nightfall they had their evening meal. Soon after that they had company.

Augustine's marriage had not parted him from his friends. Harmodius had gone to live with Alypius. Every school night the two of them came with their books to Augustine's house. They studied together and talked. Melania made them dishes of coconut paste and mixed fruit and saw to it that their wine cups were kept filled.

She was happy and Augustine was happy. Only once in a while, when he sat down to write his mother, did a frown pucker his brow. He was a wild fellow, bent on having his own way. But God had made him as He makes everyone. He had a conscience, and every now and then it twitched.

His mother still knew nothing of his marriage. His letters to her dealt mostly with what was going on at school. He was doing well there. Some of his professors thought him the brightest student they had ever had.

His mother's letters were filled with small news: Patricius, his father, was busy at his new job as city magistrate. The farm was doing better. Both his brother and sister had been baptized and confirmed. His sister—"God be thanked," his mother wrote—had discovered that she had a vocation. In the near future she would be entering an order of nuns.

Then came a letter that jolted him. Patricius had died. His mother begged him not to interrupt his studies to come home. She urged him not to think of her as grieving.

"I shall miss your father," she wrote, "but I am happy in the thought that he died a Catholic Christian. Now all my prayers are for one thing only—that you, too, will soon join the rest of your family in the Church of God."

Augustine dropped his mother's letter on the stone table by which he sat. He had come home from school earlier than usual. He was alone in the garden.

Suddenly he envied his mother. He envied her calm, firm faith. What a joy, he thought, to have a faith like that: to know that your Church was always there, ready to help, to console, to advise . . .

Springing to his feet, he made a fist of his right hand and slammed it into the other. The old question was nagging at his mind. "Why," he wondered for the hundredth time, "is there so much evil in a world made by a God Who is all good?"

He walked back and forth in the garden. Recently he had put the question to one of his professors. "You are too young," the professor had told him, "to worry about such things."

Too young! Augustine smiled bitterly. How little older people understood! As if one were ever too young to ask why, why!

Without realizing it he had dropped to his knees. He said it again, this time aloud: "Why? If You are so good, O Lord, why do You permit so much evil?" In the sudden silence following his cry, he fell face forward on the earth, bawling like a baby.

During the brief winter Augustine and Melania entertained their two friends indoors. With the return of warm weather in late February they put a coal lamp in the garden and spent their evenings there. It was a pleasant place with white blossoms dripping from the myrtle bushes and the fountain plashing in its cool depths.

There came a summer evening, hot and moist. When Augustine failed to arrive at nightfall Melania thought nothing of it. Twice lately he had been detained till shortly after dark.

She ate alone. After the dishes were washed she sat before her needlework frame in the garden.

Her hands were busy when the gate off the alley opened and Alypius and Harmodius hurried in, laughing and chattering. With exaggerated ceremony they presented her with a bottle of Falernian wine.

At first they, too, were unworried by Augustine's absence. But as darkness thickened and the hours moved on, they became uneasy. Alypius glanced at the water clock in a niche of the garden wall. He noticed that Melania was looking at it too.

"Has he ever been this late before?" he asked.

"No." Melania went on with her needlework. "It is Thursday, isn't it?"

"It is. Why?"

"He was late last Thursday, though not this late. And the Thursday before."

"Did he say what kept him?"

"A meeting. I think he said a religious meeting. I didn't ask questions. I could see he didn't want to talk. You know how he is sometimes."

"Indeed." Alypius nodded. "There's no point talking to Augustine when he's deep in thought."

"Deep in thoughts of himself, that is." Harmodius spoke dryly.

Melania gave him a jab with her needle. "Now, now!" she chided.

Harmodius gazed at her fondly. "You're an angel," he said, "but admit now, your husband is not very considerate of others."

"Let's say he finds it harder to be considerate of others than some people do." Melania smiled. "We're not all made alike, you know."

"True."

Even as Harmodius spoke, there was a firm tread in the alley. Melania rose, a half cry on her lips. When the gate opened and Augustine entered, she ran over and threw her arms around him.

"Are you all right?"

He pushed her gently aside with his free hand. The other held a large book. Moving past her, he deposited it on the stone table near the fountain. Alypius and Harmodius had never seen such a sober look in his eys. At the sight of it, their expressions of greeting died on their lips.

In the silence Melania resumed her seat. She smiled happily, her eyes on her husband's face.

He spoke finally. "Well," he said, "I've found it."

"Found it?" Harmodius was the first to recover from the general amazement at this mysterious remark.

"Yes, found it."

Harmodius leaped up. "By the shades of my

ancestors!" he exclaimed. "Augustine, I have half a mind to thrash you. You come home hours late. You know we've been worrying. Has he fallen among thieves, we've been asking ourselves. Is he hurt? Is he dead or alive?"

With a growling sound Harmodius hastened from behind the table. He faced Augustine. "And when you do arrive, what do you do? You stand before us, looking dramatic, and mumbling, 'I've found it, I've found it!' What is all this mumbo jumbo? What have you found?"

Augustine gave him a cool, sweet smile. "The answer to my question," he said.

"Oh, by the shades of everybody's ancestors! What question?"

Augustine glanced at Alypius. "He knows," he said.

But when the others turned eagerly to Alypius, his face was blank. "I'm sorry," he said. "I don't know what you're talking about."

Augustine smiled again. "Don't you remember the night we robbed the pear orchard in Tagaste?"

"I'd rather forget it if you don't mind."

"Afterwards," Augustine went on calmly, "we sat on the hillside, you and I. 'Why,' I asked you, 'is there so much evil in the world?' Remember, Alypius? I said if I ever found the answer to that

I would know what to believe. Well!" Augustine's voice rose suddenly. "I've found it!" he shouted. "I've found my religion!"

He opened the large book on the table. He riffled through some of its parchment pages. "There!" He thumped one of them with his hand. "There is the man who founded it. There is the man whose religion I shall follow from this day forth!"

Melania and the boys bent over the table. Eagerly they examined the drawing on which Augustine's hand had fallen.

It showed a slender, piercing-eyed man dressed with odd elegance. He wore a mantle of blue taffeta and shoes of different colors, one red, the other green. In his right hand he carried an ebony staff. Under his left arm was a book similar to the one at which they were looking.

Melania was the first to speak. "Who is he, Augustine?"

"Mani," Augustine told her. "He lived some five centuries ago in Persia. He was a wise man and a great artist."

"And what is the name of the religion he founded?"

"Manicheism. It is named after him."

"Manicheism?"

Melania had trouble with the word. Augustine

pronounced it for her syllable by syllable. "Man-i-KEE-ism," he said. "Those who follow it are called Manicheans—Man-i-KEE-ans."

"And Manicheism answers your question?" Alypius asked.

Augustine nodded. "The Manicheans say that the world is ruled not by one god but by two. One is good and is called the Prince of Light. The other is evil and is called the Prince of Darkness. These two are battling one another for the souls of men. When a person comes under the influence of the Prince of Light, he does good things. When he comes under the influence of the Prince of Darkness, he does bad ones."

Augustine looked around triumphantly. "And that," he declared, "explains the presence of evil in the world. It is all created by the great Prince of Darkness." He smiled happily. "Have I made it all clear?"

"I'm afraid not." It was Alypius speaking.

"Sit down then, all of you. The Manicheans hold their meetings Thursday nights. I've attended three. I'll tell you what I've learned." Augustine tapped the large volume on the table. "I'll also read you some passages from their book of wisdom."

Augustine pulled a chair to the table. He opened the book. He talked—and talked.

On Thursday night of the next week he took

Melania and the boys to a meeting of the Manicheans. There the others discovered that Augustine's new religion was more complicated than he had led them to believe. Even so, he had given them a pretty good picture of it. The Manicheans did believe that there were two almost equally powerful forces—one good and one evil. They believed that the fate of the world hung in balance while these two forces fought over the souls of mankind.

Alypius found it hard to grasp. Shortly, however, he did what he always did. Since Augustine had become a Manichean, he became one too. Harmodius had to think it all through. In the end he followed suit.

As for Melania, "To be honest," she said, as she and Augustine sat at breakfast in the sun-drenched garden one morning, "I'm not sure I even like it." She had finished eating. Rising, she crossed the garden and seated herself in an armchair near the vine-covered wall.

Augustine followed her with his eyes. "Just what don't you like about it?" he asked gently.

She blushed. "If I tell you, will you be offended?"

"No, no. What's wrong with Manicheism?"

"Well . . ." Melania uttered an embarrassed little laugh. "I think it's a bit too convenient."

"Convenient?" Augustine was puzzled.

"Yes. It's too easy. Suppose I steal or tell a lie. Those are sins, aren't they?"

"Of course."

"Well, if I do those things of my own free will, it's silly to say I'm not to blame. It doesn't seem fair to say it's all the fault of some mysterious Prince of Darkness." Augustine frowned, and Melania added hastily, "I have offended you, haven't I?"

Augustine shook his head. He shook it vigorously, but, in truth, he was a little disturbed by Melania's criticism. He decided, however, to pay no attention to it. Like many bright persons, Augustine was inclined to underrate the intelligence of others. He liked to think of his wife as a pretty little thing—but without a brain in her head. He was certain that she objected to Manicheism only because she could not understand what it was all about.

There was another reason why he could not be offended with her this morning. It seemed to him that she had become more beautiful than ever lately. There was a glow on her cheeks. He had noticed it often in recent weeks. It was as if she were hugging some wonderful secret to herself.

She dropped her eyes before his gaze. "Augustine," she said in a low voice, "soon we are going to have to tell your mother about our marriage."

"By all the heroes!" He stared at her wide-eyed. "Why do you bring that up at this time?"

"We can't keep it a secret from her much longer."

"Why not?"

"Because in a few months she's going to be a grandmother."

Augustine tried to speak, but couldn't. The words would not pass the sudden lump in his throat. When he found his voice, his words ran together.

"Oh, my darling!" he said.

"So you see, Augustine, your mother must be told. Will you write her this very day? And another thing," she went on. "Romanianus tells me you have made him a promise."

"About his boy?"

"You promised when you finished school to return to Tagaste and tutor his son for a while. Well, you'll be through in less than a year now. Are you going to keep your promise then?"

"Of course. The minute I'm graduated we'll pack up. We'll live for a while in Tagaste."

"Oh, no."

"Why do you say 'Oh, no'?"

"Because I want you to go home alone, Augustine. I want you to live for a while with your mother—just you. It will be easier that way for you to make your peace with her."

"But you and the child?"

"My mother will come here to live with us. The three of us will be quite happy waiting for you to return. Please say you'll go to Tagaste by yourself, Augustine. Things will work out better that way."

"I suppose they will."

She smiled at him. "After all," she said, "you have something else to tell your mother."

"Have I?"

"You must tell her about your new religion."

He paced away from her. Her eyes followed him. "I imagine," she said, "that your mother will find that harder to forgive than your marriage."

Augustine nodded.

"But you must tell her when you go home," his wife continued. "It's not right to keep such important things a secret from those who love you."

The summer passed and there was a long and hazy fall. In the early winter of the year 372 the child was born. It was a boy. In delight and gratitude Melania insisted on their calling him Adeodatus, which means, "a gift from God."

7. Some Sad and Some Glad Events

Autumn had come, but hot weather still hovered over the little city of Tagaste and over the plateau on which it stood. There had been a heavy rain in the late afternoon. In a reddish evening sun Augustine climbed the hill toward his mother's farm, carrying his traveling bag. The soaked earth gave like springs under his feet.

He had finished his schooling in Carthage. True

119

to his promise, he had come home to tutor Romanianus' son and to make peace with his mother. He had traveled with Romanianus in the latter's silver coach. At the big merchant's estate he had expressed a wish to walk the rest of the way by himself.

He wanted time to compose his mind. He had written his mother about his marriage. Her reply had been just what Melania had said it would be— she wished the young couple good luck. He had not told her about his new religion. He wondered how she would act when he did.

He had reached the crest of the hill. The farm lay before him. In his boyhood it had seemed a large place. It looked small to him now, as did everything in and around Tagaste. The fields were well kept. That, he knew, was thanks to his younger brother. Navigius was quiet and slow-thinking, but he was a youth of fine character and an excellent farmer.

At the front gate Augustine halted. He smiled to himself. Some day, when Adeodatus was no longer a baby, he would bring him here. He would let him swing on the gate as he had so often done in his own childhood.

Busy with his thoughts, he did not notice the slender, white-clad woman step into the doorway.

He had entered the garden and was closing the gate when he saw her.

Monica was wearing a peplus, a long gown of many folds. His first thought was that she had grown smaller in his long absence. Hurrying up the steps, he embraced her. Then, holding her at arm's length, he looked closely at her oval face.

"Greetings, Augustine."

"Greetings, Monica."

He looked beyond her into the empty atrium.

"Alone?" he asked.

"Yes. Your sister could not possibly get away from the nunnery, and Navigius is in Madaura on business. I expect him in the morning."

A manservant slipped into the atrium as she spoke. He slipped out again, taking Augustine's bag. Monica indicated a chair standing beside a small table set with wine cups and a dish of figs and dates.

But first Augustine wished to take a turn about the room, looking it over. Little had changed. There was a new marble bust on a new pedestal. He examined it for some time, thinking that the sculptor had created a good likeness of his dead father.

His mother had seated herself. He turned, facing

her across the big room. "Well, mother," he said, "am I welcome here?"

"Why, Augustine!" Her voice was full of shock. "This is your home. I hope you don't mean because of your marriage. I wrote you about that. You know that as far as your marriage is concerned I have only one wish."

Augustine nodded. "I know," he said. "You hope that some day I'll be married in the Church."

"Naturally."

"Well, that is the first thing I must tell you, mother. I will never be married in the Church."

"Never?"

Augustine crossed the room and sat down in the chair near his mother. He studied her face. He had the feeling, somehow, that she already knew about his religion. "Mother," he said softly, "are you sure you haven't heard? There's an old saying, you know, that bad news travels fast."

A trace of a smile touched Monica's lips. "Bad news?" she inquired.

"I didn't mean it the way it sounded. Of course, you might consider it bad news."

Monica nodded. "Yes, I've heard the bad news, as you call it. I've heard that you've joined the Manicheans."

Augustine sat back in his chair. He felt relieved. At any rate, he did not have to break the news.

She was looking at him in a probing sort of way. "Tell me about it, Augustine," she said. "What do the Manicheans believe?"

"Oh, goodness." He waved a hand in the air. "It's a deep religion. One could study it all his life and still not know it all."

Once again the pale smile flickered momentarily on Monica's lips. "The same could be said of Catholicism," she said dryly. "But it's a poor sort of religion unless a very child can understand the heart and gist of it. What is the gist of Manicheism, Augustine?"

"To begin with, we believe in two gods, the Prince of Light and the Prince of Darkness."

"And Christ?" his mother put in. "Where does our Lord fit into the Manichean scheme of things?"

"Oh—some Manicheans think He was a great prophet, some don't."

"But you do not think He was God?"

"No."

"And who made us, Augustine? According to your new religion, who created human beings—the Prince of Light or the Prince of Darkness?"

"Both."

"Both?" Monica's brows lifted slightly.

"Yes, both. The Prince of Light made our souls, the good part of us. The Prince of Darkness made our bodies, the bad part of us."

"Augustine!" Monica's expression was one of almost comic amazement. "How can you say that our bodies are bad? How can you speak thus of the very temples of our souls? You know as well as I do that our bodies and our souls are both good because both were created by the dear, sweet Lord. How can you believe a religion that teaches otherwise? I thought you were an intelligent man!"

Augustine leaped to his feet. Monica had hit his weak spot. She had questioned his intelligence, and Augustine considered himself just about the most intelligent person in the world.

"Stop it!" he shouted at her. "Stop lecturing me. I'm not a boy any more, and I won't be lectured to."

"Who's lecturing?" Monica looked at him in astonishment.

"You are and I want you to stop it!" He stormed away from her. He stormed back. "I'll believe what I like!" he shouted at her. "I'll believe in two gods, a hundred gods if I wish. As for your Christ, who cares about Him?"

Augustine had no sooner spoken these dreadful words than he wished he hadn't. His mother rose. He had hurt her, he could tell. He had hurt her more than he had ever hurt her before. He saw her face turn pale, becoming as white as her gown.

He saw her totter slightly. He heard her speak, saying something that he had never dreamed she could be driven to say.

"Go!" she said softly to her son. "Go, Augustine. Leave my house!"

Augustine ran. He heard the front gate close behind him. He continued to run. He ran until there was no breath in him. Falling into the thick autumnal grass, he lay with his eyes tight shut.

A strange sorrow filled him—strange, that is, for a man who thought he did not believe in our Lord. He was miserable, partly because he had hurt his mother but mostly because he had committed the sin of blasphemy.

When he opened his eyes, he saw that it was quite dark. He saw, too, that the spot was familiar. It was the hillside on which he and Alypius had rested after robbing the old farmer's pear orchard. There was the same indigo sky sprinkled with distant stars. The same cricket lullaby pierced the night air.

He rose, dusting the grass stains from his tunic. It occurred to him that he had left his bag at his mother's house. Oh, well! He would send for it tomorrow. There was only one thing to do now. He would go and live at Romanianus' house.

Romanianus was the richest man in Tagaste. A

golden dome covered the center villa of his large, walled-in estate. All around were gardens. Beyond these was a forest where gazelles roamed and where Romanianus spent much of his time hunting on one of the horses he kept in his stables.

Augustine had never lived a life of such luxury. In keeping with family custom, he rose late in the morning, going at once to Romanianus' private baths. Breakfast followed, after which he gave Romanianus' son his daily lesson.

Meals were taken Roman style. The diners lay on couches alongside a huge table in a colonnaded court of one of the gardens. After the evening meal Augustine and Romanianus talked for long hours in the fountain-cooled atrium.

Thanks to Augustine's persuasive arguments, Romanianus, too, had become a Manichean. Some evenings they read from the Manichean book of wisdom and discussed it. Some evenings they talked politics. The Roman Empire had fallen on troubled times. Dwelling in the forests of central and northern Europe were hordes of people usually spoken of as the barbarians. The barbarians were a rugged people living simple lives. Many of them occupied territory that had been seized by Rome, but they did not like Roman rule. Already there had been small rebellions. People spoke with dread of a rumor that there would be more. Some feared that eventually the barbarians would invade the great city of Rome itself. Then what?

"And then," Augustine said to Romanianus one evening, "the empire will fall."

"Oh, no!" Romanianus swept a huge arm through the air. "All the barbarians in the world will never destroy the Roman Empire."

"They won't have to. The empire is destroying itself."

"Whatever do you mean?"

"Look around you, Romanianus." With a gesture Augustine took in the immense atrium with its high columns and ivory-inlaid furniture. "We Romans have become materialists. We think of nothing but luxury."

Romanianus started to protest, but Augustine silenced him with a shake of his head. "We have become soft," he insisted. "If the barbarians ever come after us in large numbers, we will crumble before them."

He ceased speaking, his attention taken by a sound of voices in the hallway. He heard one of the slaves. Then he heard a deeper and rather solemn voice.

He jumped to his feet. "Romanianus! I could swear that voice belongs to . . ." He broke off at the sight of a dark young man coming into the room.

It was Harmodius. The two friends shook hands and embraced and shook hands again. Augustine gave his young friend an affectionate nudge. "Now tell us all the news from Carthage."

Harmodius nodded. "I'll begin with first things first."

"Do that!" Augustine cried. "Melania and the boy?"

"Both doing well. Melania's mother takes good care of them, and your son grows apace."

"Marvelous! And you, Harmodius? What are your plans now?" Augustine asked him.

Harmodius had several plans, he said. He had come home to talk them over with his parents. The mention of parents brought a pucker to Augustine's brow. Harmodius spotted it. "I dropped by your house, Augustine," he said, "but your mother told me . . ."

"Yes, yes," Augustine put in hastily. "Mother and I had a disagreement, so I'm staying here."

He noticed a questioning look in his friend's eyes, and was startled at his next remark. "You know, Augustine," Harmodius said, "I think you ought to have more respect for your mother's ideas."

"What's that?" Augustine jumped up and strode to his friend's chair. "Look here," he shouted, "you aren't thinking of becoming a Catholic?"

Harmodius nodded. "I am thinking about it, yes. I talked to my parents about it this afternoon. I told them that one of these days I wanted to be baptized."

"You're not serious!"

"Serious enough. At any rate, I intend to see the bishop and talk it over with him."

"Talk to me first." Augustine's voice rang with earnestness. "Will you do that?"

"I'm always glad to talk with you."

"Good." Augustine chuckled as he returned to his chair. "We'll discuss it some day. I'll show you the error of your ways."

Harmodius looked over his shoulder at the window behind him. "Would you mind drawing the curtains? The night air seems chill."

"Certainly, certainly." Romanianus hastened toward the window. "Strange," he added. "The night seemed warm to me."

Augustine looked with sudden concern at Harmodius' face. "Look here," he said, frowning, "are you sure you feel all right?"

"It's nothing. I have a little cold. That's all."

But it was not a little cold. In the city on an

errand the following day, Augustine heard alarming news. During the night Harmodius had been stricken with a fever and was unconscious.

Augustine wasted no time in getting out to the farm where his friend lived.

A woman servant responded to his knock. The main room was small and simply furnished. There were no statues such as cluttered his living room at home. The walls were bare save for one object— a small crucifix with a candle burning on the table below it.

Seeing it, Augustine started. Then he remembered. Harmodius had told him that some years before his father and mother had become Catholics.

He remembered too that only the night before Harmodius had talked of being baptized. But had he really meant it? Augustine had thought not at the time; he still thought not. Consequently he was shocked and puzzled at the scene that greeted him in the little bedroom to which the servant led him.

There were several people in the room. At the far side of the sleeping couch, bent and fragile in his black robes, stood his mother's close friend and spiritual director, the bishop of Tagaste.

Even as Augustine entered the room, the bishop's wrinkled hands moved in blessing above the head of the unconscious boy on the couch. Water dripped from his fingers. His lips formed the words of the ancient sacrament: "I baptize thee in the name of the Father and of the Son and of the Holy Ghost."

Anger rose in hot waves within Augustine. He advanced toward the bed. Only with effort was he able to keep his voice reasonably low.

"What is this?" he demanded.

The bishop peered at him. His old eyes were watery and weak. "Ah," he said finally, "are you not young Augustine?"

"I am he. And I am Harmodius' best friend." With a quick movement Augustine indicated the sick boy on the sleeping couch. "And I demand to know what you have done to him!"

"Done to him?" The bishop spoke with deliberation. "As Monica's son, you know very well what I have done. I have baptized him because his parents tell me that such is his desire."

Augustine turned toward the middle-aged couple standing at the foot of the bed. He saw where Harmodius got his fine, strong features. They were beautiful people. She was small, but she held her head high. The man was a handsome giant.

There was a look of great happiness in their

faces. The sight of it only fed Augustine's anger. "Why have you done this?" he cried to them. "Your son is not a Christian. He is a Manichean, even as I am. You have no right to baptize him when he is unconscious and unable to speak for himself."

"Please do not be angry." It was the woman who spoke. She smiled. "Our son told us yesterday that he wished to be baptized. We have done only what we felt we must. The doctor says our boy may die tonight. We could not let him leave this world without doing all in our power to save his soul."

Her voice was calmness itself. At another time it would have soothed Augustine, but not now. "You have no right!" he screamed at her. "No right!"

He felt a hand on his shoulder. "My boy, this is a sickroom." The old bishop spoke as before— in a low and unhurried manner. "If you cannot keep your voice down, you must depart."

Pulling loose, Augustine hurried from the house. Out in the road he kicked at every stone he saw.

Arriving home, he was told that Romanianus was resting on one of the couches in the atrium. His noisy entrance into the big room brought the wine merchant to his feet. "By the shades of my ancestors!" he exclaimed, seeing Augustine's troubled face. "Here is an angry man. What has happened?"

When Augustine told him about Harmodius' illness, the big man shook his head sadly. "I must go to him at once," he said.

"No!" Augustine restrained him with a hand on his arm. "I have not finished yet."

He told him how Harmodius had been baptized while he lay unconscious. He had expected Romanianus to share his anger. Instead, an expression bordering on amusement crossed the older man's face. "But, Augustine," he said, "why should this baptism annoy you so?"

"How can you ask?"

"But don't the Christians believe that baptism places some sort of mark on the soul?"

"So they say. They teach that baptism cleanses the soul of its sins."

"But you don't believe that, do you?"

"Of course not. Baptism is a mere superstition."

"Well, then! According to you, nothing has happened to Harmodius. You have no reason to be angry, unless . . ."

"Unless what?" Augustine demanded, seeing that the big merchant had fallen silent.

Romanianus shrugged. "Nothing," he answered.

"You were about to say something else to me, Romanianus. What was it?"

"Forget it. It would only make you angrier."

"I insist. What was it?"

"I was about to say that you do believe in baptism."

"Romanianus!"

"Hear me out, Augustine. I have watched you closely of late. You are full of doubts about Manicheism. Your mother's training is taking effect. At this moment your heart is closer to her religion than it is to your own."

Augustine only just heard the big man's last words. He had stomped from the room, shaking with anger. He knew that if he remained he might lose control of himself. He might even attack Romanianus and do him bodily harm.

In the luxurious apartment where he slept, he threw himself on the velvet-covered couch by the open windows. He was still lying there, an hour later, when a servant came to tell him that the evening meal was being served.

He sent the servant away. He had no interest in food. For long hours he tossed on his couch. Midway in the night, sheer physical exhaustion took its toll. He slept an hour or so, but his sleep was fitful and he awoke more tired than before.

Jumping from the couch, he dressed and hurried from the house. Outside he trudged along the road under a dark sky shot through with stars. The false dawn lay pasty and gray over the fields as he once more came within sight of the farmhouse where Harmodius lived.

Even before entering, he was conscious of a stir in the small dwelling. He did not bother to knock. Inside he went at once to Harmodius' room.

He halted on the threshold, a stifled cry on his lips.

Harmodius was alone in the room. He was sitting up on the bed, his back supported by a pile of pillows. He nodded brightly.

"Harmodius!" Stepping in, Augustine seized his friend's hand, crushing it in his own. "Harmodius, you are well again!"

Harmodius smiled. He rarely did so, and this morning his smile had a quality in it Augustine had never observed before. "Not quite well," he said, "but better." He pointed to a chair, indicating that Augustine should bring it over to the bed.

Augustine did so, but without taking his eyes from his friend's face. Harmodius, he could see, was not quite well yet. His dark features were still drawn. Speaking, it was obvious, cost him some effort.

Augustine seated himself. "What a great thing!" he exclaimed. "When I left yesterday, I was told you would not last until morning."

"So the doctor thought. He was surprised when he came during the night. He said it was a miracle."

"A miracle it is!" Augustine bounced with pleasure. "And now what a laugh we can have together. Do you know the many-headed goddess in the temple of Tanit in Carthage?"

"I've seen the awful monster."

"I thought you had. Now listen. Suppose a Catholic priest entered the temple of Tanit and sprinkled water on the goddess and baptized her. Would you not roar with laughter? Would you not . . . ?"

Augustine's voice trailed off. He stared at Harmodius, uncertain what to make of his suddenly grave expression. "Look here," he said. "Perhaps you already know. Have you been told that while you were unconscious the bishop baptized you?"

Reaching out, Harmodius took his friend's hand. "I have something to tell you about that," he said. "My mother told me shortly before you arrived. Strangely enough, I already knew."

Augustine withdrew his hand with a sudden movement. "You knew that you had been baptized even before you were told?" he asked.

"Not exactly. But when I came to my senses in the middle of the night, I knew that something had happened to me. I had a feeling . . ." Harmodius paused briefly. "I don't know how to describe it to you. I felt calm, very calm. I remember thinking to myself, 'I, Harmodius, have been reborn.' "

Augustine half rose from his chair. "You mean that you accept your baptism?"

The sick boy nodded. "Why are you so surprised?" he asked. "I told you I wanted to be baptized."

"I didn't think you meant it." Augustine forced his words through clenched teeth.

"But I did mean it. I am happier at this moment than I have ever been."

Augustine looked wildly around. He had the feeling that if he did not go at once he would burst into tears or tear the place apart. He had left the house before he realized what he was doing.

Outside on the road he moved at a furious pace. After a time he deserted the road, following a path across the fields. He had no idea where it went, nor did he care. He walked on and on, sometimes fast, sometimes slowly. Once, looking up, he discovered that the morning had gone. The blazing North African sun stood in the position of noon.

He went on, still without thought to direction.

He was startled suddenly to find himself passing through Romanianus' gate and walking up the steps of the main villa.

As he entered the atrium, a slender, white-clad figure came out of the shadowy alcove at the far end of the room. He stopped, hearing a familiar voice.

"Greetings, Augustine."

It was his mother. She held out her arms, and he went into them. He held her tightly for a few seconds. Her unexpected visit brought him neither surprise nor any other emotion. The events of the last two days had been too much for him. They had drained him of feeling.

He stepped back after a while, looking numbly at his mother. "What brings you to me, Monica?" he asked.

"I could not bear to think of you alone at this time. I heard about Harmodius."

"Oh, him!" Augustine waved a hand through the air. "He'll be all right now. He regained consciousness."

"But not for long."

He repeated her words mechanically. "Not for long?"

"I thought you knew, Augustine. Your friend died shortly before noon this morning."

He dropped his head. It was only a movement,

however. He still felt nothing. Later he would be overcome with grief at the loss of his friend, but at the moment he felt nothing.

He became aware that his mother had stepped closer. "Augustine," he heard her say, "I had a wonderful dream about you the other night."

"Did you?"

"I dreamed that I was standing on a huge sort of ruler. Suddenly I looked up, and there you were standing at the other end of the ruler. And in my dream I heard you speak. You said, 'See, mother, I am with you now.'"

Augustine continued to stare at the richly inlaid mosaics of the floor. "And what did you make of your dream?" he asked her.

"I am convinced that God sent it. It was His way of telling me that some day you would stand with me in my religion."

Numb as he was, Augustine could not pass up an argument. "Your dream could be interpreted another way," he said.

"Could it?"

He looked up. He saw the pale smile come to his mother's lips and linger there. "Your dream," he said, "could mean that some day you will stand with me in my religion."

Monica shook her head, still smiling. "No," she said. "In the dream you did not say, 'See, you are with me.' You said, 'See, mother, I am with you now.'" She held out her hand and he took it. "Augustine," she said, "will you come to live in your own home again?"

He nodded. "But only for a short while," he told her. "Romanianus' son is almost ready for college now. I shall remain in Tagaste only a few weeks more. Then I must return to my wife and child."

"But you will spend the rest of your time here with me?"

"Yes, mother. I shall pack later in the day."

He lowered his eyes again. Staring at the floor, he heard Monica's light step as she left the room and the house. He stood thus for some time. He wondered if his mother knew that Harmodius had died a Christian. She probably did. He wondered if she sensed that he was losing faith in Manicheism. He told himself that she probably knew all about that, too.

He closed his eyes. Instinctively he did what he always did in a moment of crisis. He prayed:

"Dear God, You see how it is with me. I am right back where I was. I still do not know what to believe. Please, God, send some light into this dark tunnel where I walk. Show me the way to the truth!"

8. Ambrose and the Arian Empress

On a Sunday morning in the spring of the year 386, a young man strolled restlessly in the garden behind a small house not far from the public square of Milan in northern Italy.

A bright sun carpeted the garden, and the morning air was soft. Where weather was concerned, Milan, standing on the rolling Lombard plateau, was a city of extremes. There had been a brief, but fiercely cold, winter. Now the long, hot summer was setting in. The mulberry trees and the poplars along the garden paths were densely leafed. A warm breeze whispered among the branches of the single fig tree near the fountain.

The strolling young man was deep in thought. Arriving near the garden wall, he halted. He could hear voices on the far side. Standing on a bench, he peered over.

There were three boys in the adjoining garden. They were playing a game called trigon. Standing at the three points of a triangle, the boys hurled a ball at one another without warning, catching it with one hand and throwing it with the other. As the young man stepped down from the bench, he heard another young voice calling his own name from somewhere in the house.

"Augustine! Augustine!"

Augustine smiled to himself. It was his son calling him. Affectionately his mind pictured the slender, awkward lad whom God and Melania had given him.

"Augustine!"

The voice came again. "I'm out in the garden, Adeodatus," Augustine called. He sat down on the bench against the wall.

The gravel of the garden path crunched under

bare feet as the boy came running. At fourteen, Adeodatus was small for his age but well built. He had his mother's large green eyes and rounded cheeks.

"Yes, son," Augustine said, "what is it?"

"Grandmother. She wants to know if you're going to Mass with her."

"Tell her not this Sunday, Adeodatus. Alypius is coming to spend the morning with me."

"I'll tell her." But the boy did not return immediately to the house. Running lightly across the intervening space, he planted himself on the bench beside Augustine. "Father," he said, "there was a long letter from mother yesterday. Did you read it?"

"Every word of it." Augustine studied the young face beside him. "Why do you ask? Was there something in the letter that bothered you?"

The young head shook vigorously. "Oh, no. Mother sounds very happy. The only thing is that —well, every time a letter comes from her I find myself wondering."

"Wondering what?"

Turning slightly, Adeodatus looked straight into his father's eyes. "Why did mother leave us, father? Why is she in North Africa when you and I and grandmother are here in Milan?"

"Adeodatus, your mother explained all that when she left. Perhaps you don't remember."

"I remember her saying that now that grandmother was here, you and I would be well taken care of. I remember her saying some other things too—things that I . . ." The boy paused briefly. "To be honest, I guess I was too young to understand what mother meant."

Augustine nodded. Almost two years had passed since Melania had left them. Two years, he realized suddenly, were a lot in a boy's life.

"It's like this, son," he said. "When I first met your mother she was studying to become a Catholic. Then we were married and, since we were married outside the Church, she had to give up the idea. Only, down in her heart she never gave it up. So, after we moved here and grandmother Monica came to make us comfortable, she decided to become a Catholic at last." He stole a glance at the boy. "Is that clear?"

"All clear." The boy nodded. "All clear, that is, except for one thing."

"And what's that?"

"Why Africa? Why couldn't mother become a Catholic here in Milan?"

"Oh, she didn't just become a Catholic. She entered a nunnery. She's a religious now."

"I know that, father. But, after all, there are nunneries here."

"True, but your mother was born and brought up in North Africa. She preferred to enter a nunnery in her native land."

Another nod from the boy. "I see," he said thoughtfully.

"Well, then!" Augustine gave his son's back a slap that propelled him to his feet. "Run along to grandmother. And you go to Mass with her, mind me now."

"Why should I?" The boy had halted a foot or so from his father.

"Adeodatus!"

"But why should I go to Mass if you don't?"

Seizing the boy's shoulders, Augustine drew him close. "Listen to me now, son, and listen closely because this is important. Where religious things are concerned, you do as your grandmother says. I don't want you growing up the way I did."

"What was wrong with the way you grew up?"

"I never knew what I believed. I still don't know. You can take my word for it, son. That's the most terrible thing that can happen to a human being. So off to Mass with your grandmother and . . ."

Augustine left his thought unfinished. A light

crunch on the gravel told him that they were no longer alone. He looked up as his mother came swiftly down the path. Monica carried herself as gracefully as ever, but the years had put heavy lines in her face and made it angular. Lately, too, it seemed to her son, her health had failed. She did not complain, but there was a hollow look about her eyes that worried him.

"You are just in time," he told her with a smile. "I was sending this young scamp in to go to Mass with you."

"And you, Augustine?"

"Not this morning, mother. Alypius is coming over."

The slightest of frowns passed over Monica's brow. "I see," she said. With a nod to Augustine, she turned to leave, stopping as Alypius appeared. He carried two books under one arm and a harpastum ball under the other.

"Greetings, all," he cried.

The years had not robbed Alypius of his fresh and open face. He had grown heavier, and there was a hint of a line or two in his forehead. But his quality was still boyish, his voice still chirpy and bubbly. He handed the ball to Adeodatus.

"For you, my fine young rascal," he said, "with my compliments."

The boy took the sand-filled ball with a smile. "Thank you, uncle Alypius."

"Don't thank me. Thank the emperor. He pays my salary." For years Alypius had been working as a lawyer attached to the imperial court. Recently the emperor had left Rome to live in Milan and Alypius had come with him. He worked now in the royal palace not far from the public square.

He grinned at Augustine. "And how is the great professor this morning?"

Augustine had come to Milan as professor of rhetoric at the imperial school, a position of considerable importance. He did not answer Alypius' question. He tapped the books under his friend's arm, saying, "Don't tell me you've found the things I've been searching for?"

"I did." With a gesture of triumph, Alypius deposited one of the books on the bench. "This one is by your very favorite author, the great Plato. And this one," dropping the other, "is by your second favorite author, Plotinus."

Augustine opened one of the books eagerly. "By all the heroes," he exclaimed. "Alypius, I have looked for these in every bookstall in Milan. Where did you find them?"

"I stole them from the imperial library."

"Stole them? You, Alypius?" It was Monica speaking.

"I was joking, fair lady." Alypius chuckled. He turned to Augustine. "As a matter of fact, these books are a gift to you, Augustine, from the empress-mother herself."

"Well, now." There was a sizable trace of vanity in Augustine's smiling face. "That was kind of the empress-mother. Very kind of her indeed."

The present emperor, Valentinian the Second, was a boy of thirteen. The real ruler was his mother, the Empress Justina. Augustine had been invited to the imperial palace a number of times. He recalled his first meeting with the empress-mother: a small woman but stately, homely but appealing. A determined woman, he had decided, noting the firm set of her chin and the quiet fierceness of her dark eyes. He had taken pains to make her like him. After all, she was the most powerful person in the Roman Empire. She could make or break a subject with a toss of her dark head.

"And how are things at the court?" he heard his mother asking Alypius.

"As they always are." Alypius shrugged. "Rumors and more rumors."

Augustine looked up from the book which he had already started to read. "What now?" he asked. "More trouble with the barbarians?"

"No," Alypius said. "The rumor now is that the empress is about to have another fight with Bishop Ambrose." He glanced at Monica. Since her arrival in the great northern city, Monica had become a close friend of the famous bishop of Milan.

She met his glance with a look of interest. "Again?" she inquired.

The word "fight" had caught the fancy of the boy at her side. "The empress and the bishop are going to fight, grandmother?" he asked. "Don't they like each other?"

Monica smiled. "It's not a matter of like or dislike. The bishop, of course, is a Catholic, but the empress-mother is an Arian."

"Arian?"

Alypius chuckled. "You're in for it, Monica," he said. "You have some explaining to do."

Monica smiled at the boy again. "The Arians," she told him, "are followers of a bishop called Arius."

"A bishop? Aren't all bishops Catholics?"

"Arius used to be a Catholic. But he left the Church to found a religion of his own. He and his followers, the Arians, do not believe in the divinity of Christ. They say our Lord is merely a demigod, that is, a half-god. They deny that He is truly God."

"A strange view!"

"The word is 'mistaken,' I believe." His grandmother gave his arm a tug. "But come, now, or we'll be late to Mass." She nodded at the young men and hurried toward the house, the boy trotting at her side.

Alypius moved away, whistling to himself. Augustine, looking up from his book, stopped him with a shout.

"One minute, my friend, before you start walking all over the place." He closed the book, inserting a finger to keep his place. "What is this new fight between the empress and the bishop?"

"The same as last year." Alypius returned to the bench where his friend sat.

"Last year?"

"Don't you remember? The empress ordered the bishop to give her one of the Catholic churches. She wanted to turn it over to some Arian priests."

"Oh, yes. Bishop Ambrose refused, and in the end the empress backed down. I thought that settled the whole thing."

Alypius shook his head. "Apparently not. The rumor now is that she's going to try again."

"The same church?"

"No. This time she wants the new church on the public square."

"The cathedral?"

"Most people, I believe, call it simply Ambrose's church."

Augustine studied the ground for a second. "And how are you betting?" he asked. "Who will win this time? The empress or the bishop?"

Alypius shrugged. "Your guess is as good as mine. You've met the empress and you've met Bishop Ambrose."

Augustine nodded. He had called a few times at the bishop's palace to pay his respects to the great Ambrose. He remembered the visits without pleasure. There were always crowds at the palace. Each time he'd had to wait in line. He remembered finally reaching Bishop Ambrose's side. He remembered Ambrose nodding to him, asking a few questions, turning then to the next person in line. Each time Augustine had come away with the feeling that Ambrose had scarcely seen him, that if they were to meet again the bishop would not even recognize him.

"Well," he mumbled, "the people love the bishop."

"Exactly," Alypius put in. "It will be the old story—the bishop and the people versus the empress and the army."

"Or, as my mother would say," Augustine

added, "the power of God versus the power of the state." His eyes returned to the book in his hand. Again Alypius wandered off, and again Augustine called to him. "Aren't you going to sit and talk a little?"

Alypius turned back. "Certainly not," he said. "When you put your nose in a book, no one can talk to you." He wandered off again.

With a chuckle Augustine resumed his reading. But not for long. The morning was warm. Shortly he leaned back against the garden wall, closing his eyes. Suddenly his mind was awash with memories.

He was only thirty-one years old, but, looking back, he seemed to have lived a century. He remembered the Carthage years after he had finished tutoring Romanianus' son in Tagaste. He had opened a rhetoric school of his own. Students had come, but most of them could not, or would not, pay. Finally, in the year 383, he and Melania and the boy had moved to Rome.

His memory of the one year in Rome was only a little more pleasant. There, too, he had conducted classes. But it had been the same story— plenty of students but not much money. Then some friends of Alypius had brought him good news. His work had attracted the attention of the imperial authorities. He had been appointed to one of the highest posts a teacher could hold in the Roman Empire. He had been named professor of rhetoric of the imperial school in Milan.

As usual, when Alypius paid a Sunday visit, the two friends made a day of it. The night turned out unusually hot. Augustine, after his friend had departed, found sleeping difficult. Lighting the oil lamp in his room, he stayed up for long hours reading. It was nearly dawn when he fell into a deep, but rather restless, sleep.

The sun was bright at the windows when he was awakened by a clamor that seemed to have taken over the house. In Roman homes noise was the rule in the morning. The slaves rose early and went about their work with a great clatter and bang. But this noise was different. There was an edge to it, a tension.

Augustine leaped from his couch and rapidly washed and dressed. He had just finished when the door curtains parted and Alypius rushed in.

Before Augustine could express surprise at his early visit, Alypius was speaking. His face, usually so calm, was alive with excitement and concern.

"Your mother, Augustine?" he cried. "Your mother and the boy. The servants tell me they're at Mass."

"Yes, yes." Augustine glanced at the water

clock on the pedestal near his couch. "They always are at this hour. Why do you ask?"

"Because it's happened, Augustine. It's happened!"

"What's happened?"

"The soldiers. The soldiers of the empress. They've marched on Ambrose's church, and the people are pouring into the public square. There's going to be a fight, Augustine. A terrible fight. If your mother is at the church, and the boy . . ."

Augustine waited to hear no more. He was out of the room, and the house, before his friend could catch his breath and follow.

Head down, Augustine ran with all his power. It was only six blocks to the square—six blocks down a tree-shaded avenue ending in a flagstone terrace overlooking the square itself.

Augustine recalled the year before when the empress had tried to seize another church outside the city walls. He remembered how the people had attacked the soldiers, striking at them with staves and flaming pine torches. There had been a bloody battle, and a noisy one.

A noisy one! He stopped running. He stood still. He leaned his head to one side, listening hard. He was only three blocks from the square now. Alypius had said that the crowd was pouring into the area. Then why was there no noise? Why could he hear nothing? He leaned his head again, listening. But he could hear nothing, nothing at all.

He hurried on, wondering—and hoping. There was already a knot of people on the terrace at the end of the avenue. Clearing the last of the houses, he pushed through. He headed for the balustrade.

He reached it and looked down. The immense square below him was empty—empty, that is, save at the far end where the soldiers of the empress stood in long ranks on the steps of the cathedral. He could see the plumes of their tall helmets waving in the breeze, the dazzle of their bucklers in the sun. Four hundred of them, at least, was his guess. He looked around, still puzzled by the absence of sound. His eyes fell on one of the other avenues leading into the square—and he understood.

The great square of Milan stood in the center of the city. A dozen of the largest avenues flowed into it like the spokes of a wheel. And in at least half of these, blackening the pavement as they moved, he could see the people slowly advancing toward the square.

The sight of them was terrifying in itself. But it was not this that brought Augustine's heart into his throat and set the blood hammering at his temples. It was the behavior of those thousands upon thousands of people. Slowly they advanced, marching in silence, in utter silence!

Augustine shivered.

He heard hard breathing behind him. Alypius had reached him.

"Do you see?" he asked in a whisper. Alypius nodded. "How can it be?" Augustine asked.

"Ambrose," was the whispered reply.

"Ambrose?" Augustine shook his head. He could not see how the bishop, or any other human being, could have brought about this incredible spectacle. He questioned Alypius with his eyes.

"After the riot . . . over the church . . . last year," Alypius was still struggling for breath, "the bishop . . . got up in his pulpit. He told the people they must never attack the soldiers again. There must be no more bloodshed. And so . . . !"

And so, Augustine thought, his spirit swelling with awe, the people come to the aid of their bishop in silence!

"Look!" He directed his friend's attention to the bishop's palace at the other end of the square opposite the church. The palace door had opened. "Ambrose!" he whispered.

But the bishop did not appear at once. Four tall men came out. On long poles, resting on their shoulders, they carried a high and bulky object that, in the distance, seemed to be a box made of cypress wood.

Again Augustine directed a questioning look at his friend. "What is it?" he asked.

Alypius shook his head. But somewhere in the little knot of spectators on the terrace Augustine heard a whisper that he took to be in answer to his question. Looking about, he saw a husky workman smiling at him. He knew him to be a workman from the garment he wore. It was a kind of tunic called the exomis. It was made so that the big man's right arm and the right half of his chest were bare, giving him more freedom for his labors.

Seeing Augustine looking his way, the workman smiled again and formed some words with his lips. "Protasius," he whispered, "and Gervasius."

"Protasius? Gervasius?" Augustine said the words after him, wondering what they meant.

"Martyrs. Two martyrs," the workman whispered to him. "Their graves were recently found after being revealed to Bishop Ambrose in a dream. The big box contains their relics."

Augustine felt Alypius' hand on his arm. Turning, he saw that the bishop had come into the square. Augustine had heard Ambrose preach many times. The bishop's voice was weak. His language was simple and his gestures few. But there was wisdom in what he said. His words had a way of worming themselves into one's mind and clinging there.

Physically, Ambrose was not an impressive man —too small, too lean, with a gaunt, lined face, old beyond its owner's years. But down there in the square, walking behind the four men and the box, he was impressive. He was glorious. Or, perhaps, it was the tall cross he bore before him that was glorious. Slowly he walked, slowly, behind the four men and their precious burden.

And now the people, or, rather, the several moving masses of them, were coming into the square. Another few minutes and all that part of the area nearest the bishop's palace would be black with them. And every minute the silence grew more intense—like a weight pressing painfully on the ears. And then . . . !

There was a stir in the little group on the terrace. Augustine saw two men hurrying down the steps leading into the square.

One was old and very tall. The other was smaller and younger. The young man held the other's arm, guiding him as he went.

Augustine turned to Alypius. "The old one's face is familiar," he said.

"It is Severus," Alypius told him. "He used to run a butcher shop in the market place."

"But Severus is blind. He went blind over a year ago."

"I know," Alypius said. "His eyes are dead."

"Then why is he joining the crowd?"

"He isn't. Can't you see? He's going to the box holding the martyrs' relics. He thinks perhaps . . ."

Alypius ceased speaking. Severus, the old butcher, had reached the box. Tall as he was, he had to stretch to touch it.

As he did so, the huge crowd behind him ceased moving. The people halted as though someone had issued an order, although no one had. The bishop halted. So did the four men bearing the box containing the relics.

Only one man moved—Severus, the old butcher. Leaping like a boy, he ran across the square, alone and unaided, in the direction of the church. There were three large fountains in his path. He skirted them readily.

And then the second miracle happened! The soldiers on the church steps broke ranks. Half of them faded to one side, the rest to the other, making a path for the old man.

And then there was a sound. It came from the old man—the joyous, thankful cry of one who has been blind and who has regained his sight. As he disappeared into the church, the march in the square resumed.

The soldiers of the empress remained where they were. Slowly the four men carrying the martyrs' relics moved into the church. The bishop followed them. As many of the people as could crowd into the building followed him. As for the rest, the thousands who could not get in, they dropped quietly to their knees on the pavement of the square.

"It is over," Alypius whispered. "The bishop has won again."

Augustine nodded. The Empress-Mother Justina, he knew, was a stubborn woman. But there was a limit. Never again, he was convinced, would she ask Bishop Ambrose to give up one of his churches.

At that moment he saw his mother. She came lightly up the terrace steps, Adeodatus trotting at her side. Augustine rushed to her, throwing his arms about her.

Monica was smiling. "Well, son?" she said.

"I saw, mother," he told her. "I saw."

"And?" she asked.

"Oh, mother, I have long believed in your God. I know He creates the laws of the universe. He can

do with them what He wills. He can work won-
ders. Only a fool would say otherwise. But even
this miracle does not answer the questions still in
my mind."

Monica's eyes turned in the direction of the
bishop's palace. "Augustine," she said, "have you
ever thought of putting your questions to Ambrose?"

"Of course. I have called on him. You know
that. His talks have helped me, and I have learned
much from his sermons. But, as for going to see him
again . . ." Augustine shook his head.

"Why not?" his mother asked.

"Because," Augustine answered, "there seems to
be a wall between the bishop and myself. He looks
at me with those strange gray eyes. I get the feeling
he regards me as an empty-head and an upstart."

"Oh, no. Ambrose thinks well of you."

"How do you know that?"

"He has told me so. However . . ." Monica's
eyes drifted again to the bishop's palace. "Since
you find it hard to talk to him, why not call on
Simplicianus?"

The name was not familiar to Augustine. "And
who is Simplicianus?" he asked.

"He is the old priest who baptized Ambrose,"
his mother replied. "He is the bishop's chief as-

sistant and confessor. He is a kind man, Augustine, and a wise one." She took her son's hand. "As a favor to me, will you talk to Simplicianus?"

Augustine nodded.

9. "Take Up and Read!"

Simplicianus lived in an old building behind the bishop's palace, a building known as the ecclesiastical monastery. Augustine called on him the next morning. The day was hot, but the long hall down which a servant led him was cool. So was the porch on which the old priest stood before a reading stand, his eyes on a large book.

He looked up as Augustine entered and dismissed the servant with a nod. He was a slight man,

163

smaller even than the bishop. His face was as wrinkled as a dried prune. It became more so as he
smiled at Augustine and directed him to a wooden
armchair. He himself sat on a bench along the inside wall.

"So you are Augustine," he said. "Your mother
said you would be calling. She says you are interested in the Church but that there are problems."

"Yes," Augustine said, "there are problems."

Simplicianus was still smiling. "Your mother,"
he said, "tells me that you have been studying the
writings of St. Paul in the Bible."

"I am also fond of the books of Plato and the
books of other authors who believe as he did."

"Good."

"Good?" Augustine looked in surprise at the old
priest. "You think it is good for me to read Plato?"

"Why should I think otherwise?"

"Because you are a Christian."

"I try to be."

"And Plato was a pagan."

The old priest chuckled. "What else could Plato
be?" he asked. "He lived 500 years before our
Lord was born. He knew nothing of the God of
Israel to Whom the Jews bore witness." Simplicianus bent forward a little, still chuckling. "All
the same," he added, "Plato was a wise man. He

sensed that there was a God. What's more, he taught that the things of the spirit are all-important." He leaned back against the stone wall behind him. "And before Plato?" he inquired.

"I was a Manichean," Augustine told him.

Simplicianus was silent for a second. "Why?" he inquired after a while. "What attracted you to the Manicheans?"

"I once thought they could explain the existence of evil."

"Ah, yes. They say evil is created by a Prince of Darkness."

"You know about their beliefs?"

"A little. But, of course, you do not hold with them any more."

"I don't know what I hold with." Rising, Augustine strode across the porch to the stone balustrade. He stood there for a time, staring at the carob trees in the garden. "There is so much confusion in my mind." He turned suddenly, facing the old priest. "When you come right down to it," he cried, "what is the difference between the Manichean Prince of Darkness and your Christian devil?"

There was another low chuckle from Simplicianus. "My son," he said, "it is not customary to speak of the devil as Christian."

Augustine smiled in spite of himself. "You know what I mean," he said. "How do they differ?"

"The devil exists, and the Prince of Darkness does not. Then, too, the Manicheans claim their Prince of Darkness is some sort of god. We know that the devil is merely a fallen angel. True, an angel is more than man, but he is infinitely less than God."

"And evil?" Augustine shot the words at the old man. "How do you account for evil in a world made by a God Who is all good?"

Simplicianus met the young man's heated question with another of his quiet smiles. "What kind of evil do you mean?" he asked.

"What kind? Are there two kinds?"

"You know there are. Suppose, a few minutes from now, lightning should strike you. Would you not say that an evil thing had happened to you?"

"Of course, but it would not be my fault."

"Quite so. One kind of evil—the evil we call misfortune—is often nobody's fault. People suffer many misfortunes, and nobody knows why. We know only that God has His reasons. After all, He suffered for us. It is only right that we should suffer for Him." The old priest rose, moving deliberately across the porch. He stopped by the

reading stand and rested a hand on it. "But of
course," he added, turning toward Augustine,
"that is not the kind of evil you mean, is it?"

"No. I mean the evil men do. I mean sin. How
do you account for that? Why does God permit
sin?"

With a smile, the old priest spoke two words in
a gentle voice. "Free will," he said.

"Free will?" A puzzled frown locked Augustine's brows. "Free will?"

Simplicianus nodded. "God does not permit sin
directly, Augustine," he said. "He merely permits
us to choose."

"To choose?"

"Yes, son, to choose. God is not a Caesar. He is
not a sort of large-scale Empress Justina. God
wants us to be good, but he does not *force* us to be
good. To every one of us He has given the great
gift of freedom of choice."

The old man dropped his voice a little as he
went on. "Yes, Augustine," he said, "every day of
your life, every minute of the day, God permits
you to make a choice. You can obey his laws and
do good. Or you can disobey them and do evil.
You can live according to His will or according to
your own."

"In short," Augustine murmured, "you can dwell in the city of God or in the city of man."

The priest nodded. "That is well said, my son," he declared.

"But God Himself then does not create evil, does He?" Augustine went to the priest as he spoke.

Simplicianus shook his head. "Of course not. How could God, being all good, create evil?"

"Then what is evil?"

"Nothing."

"Nothing?"

"I know of no better definition of it. For example, I put my hand in yours." The priest did so as he spoke. "Now what do you feel?"

"I feel your hand, of course."

"But now I withdraw my hand." Simplicianus did so. "And now what do you feel?"

"Nothing."

"Quite so. But note this, Augustine. In withdrawing my hand, I did not create the nothing you feel. To create is to bring something into being; it is impossible to create nothing. The nothing you felt simply came about as the result of my withdrawing my hand. So it is with sin. Sin results when good is withdrawn. Sin is the absence of good. As the darkness of night is merely the absence of the sun, so sin is merely the absence of the light of God."

The old man's mild eyes were on Augustine, but Augustine's were elsewhere. He was looking beyond the priest at the porch wall. He felt the old man's hand on his shoulder. It rested there briefly and as light as a bird. "Have I been of any help to you, my son?" he heard him say.

Augustine nodded. "Thank you," he said. "I'll go now. I won't bother you further."

He went home quickly. The house was quiet, for the hottest part of the day had arrived. His mother, he knew, would be resting at this hour. He stopped a manservant in the hall, asking where Adeodatus was.

"He has gone next door," he was told, "to show his new ball to his young friends there."

Augustine hurried to his room, but the room was hot. He knew that if he lay down he would not sleep. He seized a book from the table. It was the writings of St. Paul. Stuffing it under his arm, he hurried away.

His mind was in turmoil. So that was the answer to his question! Evil—sin—was not something created by God. It was simply the result of man's disobedience to God's law.

Coming into the garden, he was surprised to see

Alypius sitting on the little bench under the fig tree. Alypius came running. He stopped short a few feet away, staring in amazement.

"Whatever is the matter with you?" he asked. "Your face is as white as a sheet."

"It is nothing."

"You're sick. I'll get a doctor."

"You will not!" Augustine seized his friend who was about to run into the house. "I *am* sick, Alypius. But can't you see? It's not my body that is sick. It is my soul. Leave me alone. I want to think." He pushed his friend aside and strode away, going the whole length of the garden and back.

He flung the book of St. Paul's writings under the fig tree and paced again, ignoring Alypius who stood watching him with a distressed face. Simplicianus' words kept running through his head. "Every day of your life, every minute of the day, God permits you to make a choice. . . . You can live according to His will or according to your own!"

Simplicianus' statement was the truth, all right. It was the truth he had been looking for all his life. And now that he had found it, he almost wished he hadn't.

He groaned aloud, pacing back and forth across the garden. A strange sort of prayer bubbled to his lips. "O, God," he prayed, "make me good—but not yet!"

Not yet!

"Every day of your life," Simplicianus had said, "every minute of the day, God permits you to make a choice."

Augustine's mind went back over his own life. He tried to think of once, just once, when he had chosen to act according to God's will. "Never!" he told himself, perhaps with more vehemence than accuracy. "Never! Never once have I followed God's will. I have always followed my own."

He remembered lying, cheating, losing his temper—all for the purpose of gaining his own ends. He remembered the night of his departure for Rome. His mother had wished to travel with him. He had told her that the ship would not leave until the next morning. He had taken her to a chapel on the docks of Carthage and left her there. Then, gathering together his wife and son, he had boarded the ship and sailed away, leaving Monica behind.

Why? Why had he lied to his mother? Simply because, at that time, he had not wished to be bothered with her!

Again he groaned aloud, pacing back and forth. "Every day of your life, every minute of the day . . ." Simplicianus had said. It was the truth.

He had found the truth! Now only one question remained—did he have the courage to live according to the truth he had found?

"Augustine!"

Augustine had come to a halt by the fig tree. He heard his friend call and saw him approaching.

"Can't I help, Augustine?" Alypius pleaded. "Isn't there something I can do for you?"

"I'm all right, Alypius." Augustine's eyes were on the book of St. Paul's writings lying on the grass at his feet.

He looked up suddenly, a startled expression on his face. From beyond the wall, in the adjoining garden where Adeodatus and his friends were playing, came a childish voice. "Take up and read!" the child was crying. "Take up and read!"

Augustine looked at Alypius with a creased brow. "Alypius," he said, "do you know any game in which the boys cry 'Take up and read?'"

"No," Alypius said.

Augustine leaned down and picked up the book of St. Paul's writings. "Alypius," he said, "I am going to open this book. After all, it is the Bible. It is the word of God. I am going to drop my hand on a line, and then I am going to do whatever that line tells me to do."

He opened the book. He dropped his hand on

the page and took it away. Then he handed the book to Alypius, pointing to the line on which his hand had fallen.

Alypius read the line:

Not in revelry and drunkenness, not in . . . wantonness, not in strife and jealousy; but put ye on the Lord Jesus Christ.

He glanced at Augustine. "And now," he said, "what is it exactly that you are going to do?"

"Just what the line says," Augustine replied. "And you, my friend?"

Alypius pointed to the line immediately following the one he had just read. "I will obey that," he said, reading the line to Augustine:

Now him that is weak in faith, take unto you.

The friends exchanged glances. Augustine's face was calm now, and he was smiling. Quietly they walked toward the house. Monica would be the first to know that her son—and with him his friend Alypius—had been converted to Catholicism. The lost sheep had returned to the fold.

And there was great rejoicing in heaven!

10. The People's Choice

On the night before Easter—April 24, 387—Augustine, his friend Alypius, and his son Adeodatus were baptized. For months they had devoted most of their time to religious study. They had ceased to be catechumens. They had become "competents," the name given to those who were ready to be received into the Church.

The ceremony took place in the cathedral on the public square in Milan. The vast building was crowded. Since there were no seats, the people knelt on a wooden floor splendidly carved with scenes from the life of King David.

Augustine, Alypius and Adeodatus were not the only competents. Together with many others they bowed their heads over the communion rail. In a silence broken only by the quiet roll of his own voice and the guttering of the candles, Bishop Ambrose moved along the sanctuary side. To each of the competents he put the same questions.

"Do you," he said, coming last of all to Augustine, "believe in God, the omnipotent Father?"

"I do," Augustine responded.

"Do you believe in Jesus, Son of God?"

"I do."

"Do you believe in the Holy Ghost?"

"I do."

In silence the bishop's assistants led the competents to a large basin. There each was lowered bodily into deep water, for this was the method of baptism used by Bishop Ambrose, a method known as immersion.

When it was over, the people sang the *Te Deum*, a hymn composed a few years before by a saintly musician and poet named Nicetas. In an organ-like surge of sound, the voices of the congregation lifted in the closing stanza:

Spare Thy people, Lord, we pray,
   By a thousand snares surrounded.
    Keep us without sin today,
     Never let us be confounded.
Lo, I put my trust in Thee;
   Never, Lord, abandon me.

Early the next week Augustine prepared to say good-by to Milan. He had resigned from the imperial school and Alypius had given up his post at the royal palace. Having become Catholics, the two men had decided to go one step further. Their plan was to take Adeodatus and some friends, return to Tagaste in North Africa, and there open a monastery.

Monica traveled with them. It was a sunny June morning when they left Milan. Nightfall of the following day found them in Ostia, the little town on the Tyrrhenian Sea which the emperors had built to protect the nearby city of Rome and to serve as its seaport.

In Ostia they met with delay. No ships, they learned, would be sailing for North Africa in the near future. They had to take lodgings in a building near the harbor and wait.

Monica was not well. On their fifth day in Ostia she was stricken with a fever that sent her son rushing for a doctor and a priest. The doctor, when he entered the sick room, shook his head.

"Your mother," he told Augustine, "will not be with you much longer."

That night the last rites were said. But the next morning Monica rallied and seemed much better. Later in the day she asked to be moved into the atrium of the flat. There, resting on a linen-covered couch, she could gaze through the big windows into a garden whose tall date palms framed the shimmering waters of the harbor.

It was a pleasant room. Augustine spent most of his time there. Sometimes he and his mother talked. Sometimes, seated at a table near one of the windows, Augustine worked on a book he had started writing some time before.

He was occupied in this way on the afternoon of the ninth day of his mother's illness. From time to time, looking up from the table, he glanced at her. Monica's eyes were closed. He was startled when suddenly, and without opening them, she spoke.

"And now, Augustine," she said, "are you quite happy?"

"Oh, yes, mother." He took his chair over to the couch and sat down beside her. "You know I am. I have only one sorrow now."

"And what is that?"

"Your illness." He bent toward her, speaking earnestly. "Mother, I pray that God keeps you with us at least until we have returned to Tagaste."

"Why do you hope that?"

"Because of something you said years ago."

"Something I said?"

"Yes, mother. You said when you died you wanted to be buried in your native land."

"How foolish of me."

"Foolish?" Augustine stared at his mother.

Her eyes were still closed. "I know better now," she said. "I know that it doesn't matter where a person is buried. One part of the world is just as close to God as any other part. When I die, son, bury me here in Ostia."

"But, mother, you may live for many years and . . ." Augustine fell silent, for Monica had opened her eyes. At the sight of the quiet joy in them, all thought of sorrow and death fled from his mind.

She reached out, taking his hand. "I shall die very soon," she said quietly. "There was a time when I asked God to keep me here. I wanted to remain on earth long enough to see you become a Catholic Christian. But now . . ." She released his hand and smiled. "My work on earth is done now. I have no further reason for living."

Monica sat up, and Augustine arranged the pillows behind her. For an hour or more they talked of the faith they now shared.

It was a talk that Augustine would never forget. Years later, recording the events of his life, he would write down his impressions of it. He would describe how, for a short spell that afternoon, it seemed to him that he was no longer held to earth by the weight of his human body. He would describe how invisible wings seemed to lift his spirit close, very close, to God.

It was his last talk with his mother. That night, quietly and with great dignity, Monica died.

Adeodatus was at the bedside, along with Augustine and Alypius. When the boy saw what had happened, he burst into loud sobs.

"Quiet, son," Augustine whispered.

"But how can I be quiet? Grandmother Monica has left us. She is dead!"

"No, son, she is not dead. She has simply left the Church Militant, which is here on earth, for the Church Triumphant, which is in heaven."

The summer passed and the winter, and still another summer, before at long last it was possible to book passage to North Africa. In Tagaste, in an old house provided by Romanianus, the long-dreamed-of monastery was set up.

Happy days followed for Augustine—happy, that is, except for a period of great grief in the year 389 when Adeodatus suffered a sudden illness and went to join his grandmother.

Augustine loved the life of the monastery. He loved the long hours of prayer and quiet thought. He wrote many books. Soon his name was known throughout the Roman Empire. From cities all over North Africa came requests that he preach to the people.

Sometimes he accepted these invitations, sometimes not. In those days bishops were not always appointed by the Church as would be the case in later centuries. Sometimes when a bishop died the people of the diocese held a meeting and elected one of their number to take his place.

Because of this custom, Augustine took care never to go to a town where the bishop had recently died. He was fearful that the people might try to make a bishop of him, and he had no wish to leave the peace of the monastery.

In the spring of the year 391, he received an invitation from Hippo, a pleasant seaport on the Mediterranean some hundred miles west of Carthage. He accepted gladly. He knew that Valerius, the bishop of Hippo, was very much alive. What he did not know was that Valerius was old and sick. For some time he had been looking for a young priest who could help him with his endless chores and take over the diocese when he died.

In Hippo, Augustine's talk drew too large a crowd for him to speak inside the cathedral. He spoke from the steps, and the people assembled in the square on the waterfront.

Augustine talked on a subject close to his heart. He told his listeners that no man could hope to reach heaven without sanctifying grace. Such grace, he said, is a gift from God to be obtained by prayer. Toward the end of his sermon, he talked a little about his own conversion.

"There was a time," he said, "when I ran feverishly after the things of this world. Riches and fame and glory—I thought those things spelled happiness. Now I know otherwise. Rich or poor, famous or unknown, a man is happy only when he lives close to God and according to His will."

Augustine lowered his head. The closing words of his speech were a little prayer. "Thank You, God," he said, "for bringing me home. Thank You for all the sinners who have repented and who will repent in the days to come. I know now that in one respect all of us here on earth are just alike—our hearts are restless, dear Lord, until they rest in Thee."

There was a silence when he finished. Then suddenly there was a stir among the crowd. Augustine heard his own name going from person to person. Far out in the sea of people in the square a slender young workman leaped onto a bench.

"Make Augustine priest!" he shouted. "Make him assistant to the old bishop!"

Augustine threw up his hands, crying "No! No!" But his voice was lost in the cheering of the people as, one by one, they took up the young workman's words and repeated them in a swelling chorus:

"Make Augustine priest! Make him assistant to the old bishop!"

In panic Augustine ran across the steps to where Bishop Valerius was standing. "Stop them, your lordship!" he pleaded.

But the old bishop was shaking his head. "I am old and sick," he told Augustine. "I can no longer perform all my duties. As a result, people are leaving the Church here in Hippo, and . . ."

"But don't you understand?" Augustine broke in. "I am content in the monastery in Tagaste. I am a simple lay brother. I wish to live and die a lay brother."

Again Bishop Valerius shook his head. "You must do as the people ask," he cried. "Otherwise still more of them will leave the Church, and their souls will be on your conscience!"

Augustine argued violently but in vain. Within a week he had been ordained. Some months later he was consecrated, becoming Valerius' auxiliary bishop. Five years later, in 396, old Valerius died, and Augustine succeeded him as bishop of Hippo.

11. The Death of a World

. . . it was cool and pleasant in Hippo on the August morning *anno Domini* 400 when Bishop Augustine finished writing the story of his life, the book he called *My Confessions*.

For almost an hour he sat in the cathedral sanctuary, thinking over the events he had described in his book. Lost in memory, he was startled suddenly to discover that the church was filling with people. A shuffling sound told him that Brother Porter, who always served his Mass, had entered the sacristy and was getting ready.

After Mass, the bishop returned to his bedroom-study. There he gathered together the pages of his manuscript. Later he would send them to the scribes for copying.

A busy day lay ahead. His diocese was large, his duties numerous. First there was a score of letters to be taken care of. A farmer wrote, asking the bishop's advice about a touchy matter. The farmer needed laborers to help with the harvest. Unfortunately the only laborers in his neighborhood were pagans. Could he, a Christian, hire such men to work for him?

Augustine, smiling to himself, wrote the farmer a letter. He told him it was quite all right for him to hire the pagans. "And while they are living with you," he suggested, "treat them with kindness and with love. In this way you will set an example of true Christian living. Who knows? Perhaps some of them, seeing how rightly and happily you live, will go and do likewise."

Augustine's eyes moistened as he picked up the next letter. It was a long parchment, covered with a neat and familiar writing.

It was from Alypius. Like himself, Alypius had not been allowed to remain a lay brother. When the bishop of Tagaste died, the people there had made Alypius their bishop.

Augustine read his old friend's letter slowly.

Then he wrote him a long reply. He began his letter in the usual way:

"To my honored brother in Christ and fellow-presbyter, Alypius, Augustine sends greeting in the Lord."

He told Alypius that he had finished his book and hoped soon to send him a copy to read. "Yes, my good friend," he wrote, "God has seen fit to send much happiness to you and me. As I sit here, I cannot help but wonder what He has in store for us during the years to come."

For Augustine, and for Alypius, too, God had many eventful years in store. Busy years. The Catholic Church was growing, but numerous ills beset it. The pagan religion was dying, but other heresies remained and new ones were always arising. Many people still followed the Manicheans and the Arians. Over the years Bishop Augustine wrote more than three hundred books, many of them aimed at pointing out the errors of these and other heretical beliefs.

Ills beset the Roman Empire, too. In the year 410 a huge army of barbarians invaded the city of Rome itself. When they left, much of the imperial city lay in ruins. In the year 430 another body of barbarians, the Vandals, left their homeland in Spain, crossed the Mediterranean, and invaded North Africa.

Three months later the Roman army under the generalship of Count Boniface retreated to Hippo, taking refuge behind its stout walls. The Vandals followed, laying siege to the western approaches of the city.

Within days after the siege began, Bishop Augustine fell ill. He was old and tired. His doctors held out little hope for his recovery.

News of his illness traveled fast, adding to the people's terrors. In the forum Count Boniface mounted the stone platform to address his army.

"My men," he said, "you have heard that the bishop is dying. You have heard, too, that some people say that the Roman Empire—the world that our ancestors built—is dying with him. But I say to you, take heart. Fight as you have never fought before. Let us strive for victory; and if we meet defeat in its place, let us meet it like men and Romans!"

In the bishop's little bedroom-study all was quiet. A number of priests stood around the couch on which he lay. Among them was Alypius, who had traveled hurriedly from Tagaste on hearing of his friend's illness.

Bending over the couch, Alypius awakened the sick man with a touch of his hand. "Augustine," he whispered, "the siege grows worse. Any day now the Vandals will enter the city and then . . ."

He ceased speaking, for Augustine had reached out for his hand. Sick as he was, the bishop of Hippo could still smile. "Alypius! Alypius," he murmured. "I believe you are still the world's champion gloom-spreader."

"Yes, yes, Augustine. I have many faults, but we can discuss those later. Right now I want your promise."

"My promise?"

"That you will leave Hippo while it is still possible to slip a person through the eastern gate."

"Leave Hippo!" Augustine sat bolt upright on his couch.

"Yes, Augustine. The Vandals know the people love you. The minute they force the gates they will come here. They will kill you first of all."

"Leave Hippo!" Augustine thundered again. "And if I do so, Alypius, where will you go?"

"Oh, it would never do for both of us to leave. It would attract too much attention. I shall remain here."

"I'm glad to hear that, Alypius, for I should miss you if you left."

"But, Augustine, a fast coach is ready. Our plan is to send you to Carthage where you will be safe."

"But I am not the bishop of Carthage. I am the bishop of Hippo, and as long as God lets me live, I intend to *stay* in Hippo!"

Augustine's voice was strong, but it was weaker the following day, much weaker the next. And, on the morning of August 28, 430, Bishop Augustine died, quietly and with dignity as his mother, St. Monica, had died before him.

Alypius looked across the couch at Brother Porter, now a very old man with almost a hundred years of living behind him. He saw the old man's lips form some words, intended apparently for himself. He leaned toward him. "What is it you are trying to tell me, Brother Porter?" he asked.

"That you are the only bishop here now," Brother Porter replied. "It is you who must go and tell the people."

"Ah, yes." Alypius nodded. He must go out shortly to the steps of the cathedral and tell the people that their bishop had died. He knew what he would say to them. He would say, "True, he is gone, but remember that his prayers are still with you—and will be through all eternity."

And Alypius' face, still boyish within its framework of gray hair, twisted as the tears gushed from his eyes. He knew that Augustine had merely gone to join the Communion of the Saints. But Alypius was wonderfully human; and the human side of him grieved, and would never cease to grieve, over the loss of his great, good friend.

VISION BOOKS

All Vision Books have full color jackets, black and white illustrations, sturdy full cloth bindings. Imprimatur.